Pov
of
Steam

Men of Steam in Action
by

Raymond Flint

SANTONA PUBLICATIONS
HULL
1996

Cover Design
Original watercolour

Out of the Darkness
by *Adrian P Thompson*
Water Colour Artist (Hull)

British Library Cataloguing-in-Publication data.
A catalogue record for this book is available from the British Library.
Copyright © 1996 by Raymond Flint.
First Published in 1996 by
Santona Publications, 3 Lawson Close, Hull HU6 7UW.

Printed and bound by IMAGE COLOURPRINT, HULL.
ISBN 0 9507960-3-4

Also by the same author
The People's Scenario 1982
The March of the History Animal 1985
Men of Steam 1994
Head of Steam 1995

The Spirit of Santona
Onward to the Horizon

SANTONA PUBLICATIONS
HULL

DEDICATED
to
JOAN

my wife of forty-six years
without whom this
book would never have been written
and
whose response when I was diagnosed as having

PARKINSON'S DISEASE
was
"We'll have to think of it as just another adventure"

PREFACE

This volume marks the completion of a 'Yorkshire Trilogy of Steam', a presentation which, hopefully, will feed that magic of steam railway nostalgia which grows stronger with each passing day.

The prominence of Yorkshire and the North-Eastern region of England as birthplace and cradle of the World's railway system is well established. The successful union of rail and steam locomotive at Stockton and Darlington in 1825 is undisputed as the World's first such achievement. The industrial fate of Yorkshire, its people and vast export industries was decided by the development of the railways.

The critical link in the development of the steam locomotive and rail in Yorkshire and the North-East is there for all to see.

The publication of the rail map 'Men of Steam Country' in this volume is intended for readers not familiar with the one-time railway topography of Yorkshire.

Those 'Men of Steam' were rugged and difficult, loyal and committed. They didn't love their locomotives but they respected them and cared for them and bled as the scrap yards devoured them. I recall them to our collective memory as their craft drifts into the mists of time being sustained only by enthusiasts, preservation railways, museums and the powerful nostalgia for steam locomotion.

It has been my fortune to receive many letters from readers of 'Men of Steam' and 'Head of Steam'. I have tried to reply to them but may not always have done so. The letters provided a lot of inspiration and sustained a determination to continue to write.

I record my thanks to all who have helped in any way with the creation of the present volume 'Power of Steam'. I hope the following text meets with their and your approval.

Ray Flint. Nov. 1996

YORKSHIRE

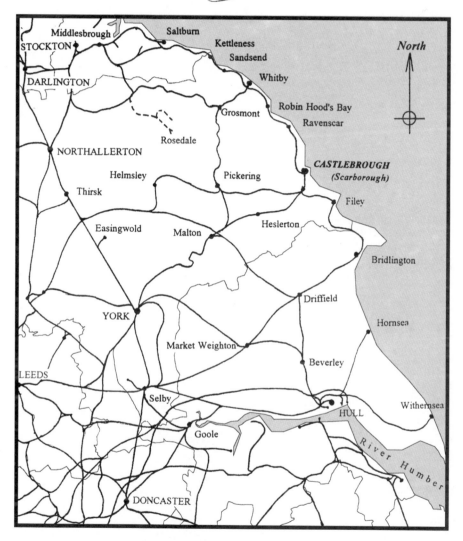

North

Middlesbrough	Saltburn
STOCKTON	Kettleness
	Sandsend
DARLINGTON	Whitby
	Grosmont
	Robin Hood's Bay
Rosedale	Ravenscar
NORTHALLERTON	
Helmsley	Pickering
Thirsk	*CASTLEBROUGH*
	(Scarborough)
	Filey
Easingwold	Heslerton
Malton	
	Bridlington
YORK	Driffield
	Hornsea
Market Weighton	
LEEDS	Beverley
Selby	Withernsea
	HULL
Goole	*River Humber*
DONCASTER	

MEN OF STEAM COUNTRY

POWER OF STEAM

CONTENTS

Dedication   5
Preface   6
Men of Steam Country   7

PART ONE: DRAMA ON THE PEAK
1   Doctor on the Line   11
2   When the Boiler Blew   21
3   Who holds the Baby?   28
4   It's Snow Excuse   33

PART TWO: ON TRIAL
1   Showing Initiative   45
2   Judgement Day   55
3   Victory Day   59

PART THREE: TROUBLE AT T' SHED
1   Election Fever   65
2   The Red Flag   75
3   Gun Fever   83

PART FOUR: POETRY, POLITICS AND PEOPLE
1   Poetry in Motion   91
2   Atomic Happenings   96
3   Displaced Persons   108

PART FIVE: NEARLY WHEELED OUT
1   Not Tyred Enough   118
2   Too Tyred   130
3   Tyred Out   134

PART SIX: OUT OF THE DARKNESS
1   Nightmare in the Snow   138
2   The Rescue   150
3   Full Steam Ahead   155

1
Doctor on the line.

"You'd think someone would be there to answer the phone," said Doctor Earnshaw, dressed in Harris tweeds and impatiently agitating the telephone bell in Robin Hood's Bay signal cabin. He stamped his feet to shake loose the knee-high snow on the lace-up shin boots.

"Are you giving the right code?" asked the porter signalman in charge of the cabin. "Here, let me try Doctor."

"Okay. By gum, it's raw today. Even for January." Doctor Earnshaw shuddered in response to the bitter cold. "They say the sea's frozen at Dover. Twenty below they say." He paused and handed over the ear-piece. "Pity that poor woman giving birth on the peak. Unheated bedroom no doubt. Mrs Black it is. Wife of one of the station staff. She won't be in Raven Hall Hotel. That's sure."

"Proper poorly they say she is," responded the porter signalman.

"Yeh. They wouldn't have asked me out if she wasn't." The doctor's habit of speaking in short crisp Yorkshire sentences seemed strange coming from a learned man. "From the Bay to the peak in all this snow. Three miles up that bank. I wouldn't be going if she wasn't desperate." His close fitting peaked cap and ear-guards were of light brown Harris tweed to match the rest of his suit. White stubble on his round chin helped advertise his age.

"Good job the ploughs are out to clear the line. You'd never get up that bank without them. Hear that? They're on line now from Whitby," replied the tall thin signalman, reaching over to his signal instruments and sending acceptance of the 'on line' audible signal he was receiving. "What's matter with the lady, Doctor?"

"She's in labour, a long labour. Complications. Sounds like a breech birth. Fancy, the Observer Corps and some West Riding Yeomanry in billet at Raven Hall and no doctor there or in Ravenscar village. What a way to fight a war? No doctor on an important headland like the Ravenscar peak. I ask you?" Diminutive Ron Sedgefield, the station master, entered noisily through the door of the signal box, banged his feet on the floor to rid his wellington boots of snow and apologised. "Sorry Doctor Earnshaw. I meant to meet you as you came up from your place and ring Ravenscar for you. Ever so sorry, but I had an important coal sale to deal with, for the school house. School's open and they were out of coal."

"That's alright Ron," replied the doctor. "I can't go anywhere until the train comes. Road traffic can't get through, again, I should say, the roads out of Robin Hood's Bay have been blocked for four days."

The station master grunted an acknowledgement in the direction of the doctor and then fired a question at the porter signalman. "Can't you get through to the peak, Robert?" He noted the shaking head. "You don't think the lines are down, do you?"

"Well, the block system's working. I've just put a train on offer and he replied."

"There he is!" exclaimed the station master in unison with a similar remark from the signalman as the answering ring sounded.

Doctor Earnshaw addressed the station master while Robert conversed on the telephone with the signalman at Ravenscar peak railway station. "Do you think we're going to get up to the peak in all this snow?" the doctor asked. "The signalman said that the snowploughs are out."

"Yes, they're on line from Prospect Hill. That's Whitby," replied the the station master. "Two big boxploughs with two locos. Gangs of men in the boxploughs too, for digging out. They'll get you to Ravenscar peak."

"That's fortunate," Doctor Earnshaw replied. "Mrs Black's in a bad way. No proper midwife with her either. Just two ladies who stand by for this sort of thing. They called me on the G.P.O. line at home. Panicking, they were, the baby's laid wrong. Looks like a breech. Hope I'm not long."

"These ploughs'll get you through. They've swept from Pickering and over Goathland summit to Whitby, now they're going to Ravenscar and Castlebrough. They'll get you through," added the station master.

"That's comforting. Am I First Class?" asked the smiling doctor fingering his white stubble.

"You're a first class passenger, Sir. But you'll be travelling rough class this time," chuckled the porter signalman.

"There aren't any carriages on the ploughs, Doctor," added the station master. "Only places for riding are on the engines or in the boxploughs with the snow gang."

"Can you play solo or dominoes?" asked the signalman still nursing the phone in contact with Ravenscar signal box. "If you can, watch your money if you ride in the plough with the men, They're good at gambling on cards and dominoes. You're wanted on the peak are you?"

"I'm not going on my holidays," replied the doctor in the same spirit. "I'm on a mission of mercy."

"Here Doc, will you take the phone? He's here." The signalman spoke again into the phone mouthpiece. "Yes Ravenscar. I can hear you. I've got Doctor Earnshaw here for you." The doctor took the phone as the distant whistle of the snowplough's locomotive carried from the north over the heavily snow-covered fields and railway lines to the signalman's ear. Whilst the doctor passed a message via the Ravenscar station cabin for the two ladies caring for Mrs Black, Ron Sedgefield and the signalman looked out in the direction of the approaching snowploughs.

The snow-fall during the night had been very heavy, two feet lay where it had fallen evenly, where it had drifted it lay thick and created virtually impassable areas. A small number of platelayers were working to clear snow and ice from points and signal wires but the large plough was necessary to cut a passage through the station. Snow was falling in large flakes, borne on a biting northerly wind. The distant train whistled as it emerged as a shadowy snow-blurred image on the bank top approaching Robin Hood's Bay from the direction of Whitby. Black smoke and exhaust steam pounded skywards. The platelayers' look-out blew his warning horn to alert the men to the danger of the approaching train. Snow flew from the sides of the forward plough to be thrown and piled to either side of the single track. The two locos exhausted energetically and black smoke was dispersed by the gale as they forced the large boxplough through the thick drifts and cut a passage into the station.

In the signal cabin Doctor Earnshaw was in telephone conversation with Ravenscar preparing his listener to carry brief instructions to Mrs Black and her family. Privately he cursed the absence of a midwife at Ravenscar. If there had been one he might have avoided being called out, but he had fears, from the panicky voices on the phone line, that the birth was going to be complicated.

The station became a busy noisy place as the two grey-blue boxploughs and the two attendant locomotives charged between the two platforms and threw the five-feet of drifting snow to either side. The expelled snow fell heavily on the small station buildings and platforms. With chimney heads roaring exhaust steam and the engine whistles screaming warnings to all about, the two ploughs and locos continued through the station and halted on the single line that led to Ravenscar station, three miles to the south on the 600 feet high coastal peak on the Yorkshire Moors. They reversed and with similar effort swept back into the station down the neighbouring platform. Another reverse and they pulled into Robin Hood's Bay station drawing to a halt alongside the platform. The first engine, a J21 with a throbbing donkey engine at work maintaining pressure for the Westinghouse brake system, needed to fill its tank from the mushroom shaped water column. The fireman, overcoated and gloved, with a knitted balaclava protecting him from the wind-driven snow, climbed along the top of the tender to place the frozen water-hose in the tank.

★ ★ ★ ★

Three miles distant to the South at Ravenscar, four dark figures toiled on the snow-blanketed lines and platforms, clearing point rods and signal wires, trying to make them operational for the promised snowploughs coming from Robin Hood's Bay.

"Let's have a brek an' a cuppa in the signal cabin," shouted the ganger to his men. "It'd freeze t'horns off a bullock."

They were welcomed by the station master, who greeted them with, "Come on in get a cup o' tea lads. I just saw three blackfaced sheep on the other end of the platform. Better watch for them when the ploughs come."

"Lookin' fer shelter. It'll be hell out there on the moors in this blizzard. When I go down I'll see if I can chase 'em into the old barn," responded the ganger as he and the three men pushed into the warm cabin.

The view from the cabin did not extend far because of the density of falling snow. The cliff edge and Raven Hall Hotel were hidden in the distance behind the descending snow. The signal post, with its horizontal red semaphore signal, could be seen in the direction of the tunnel, but the tunnel mouth, only yards further on, was lost in the white blanket. "The tunnel mouth's about blocked off wi' snow. We'll have to try an' shift a bit afore the ploughs come through," continued Blaster Baines the ganger. "Don't want him sticking in t'hole afore he gets through to clear the station."

"They'll mek it. Them ploughs with two engines tek a bit o' stopping." The Ravenscar station master paused while he poured boiling water on the tea leaves in the pot. The four platelayers were banging their hands and preparing for a smoke. "When he gets through here he'll have no difficulty going downhill to Stainton Dale and on to Castlebrough. Then the line'll be open to the regular services."

"The Doc's a comin' with the ploughs, isn't he?" questioned Blaster Baines.

"Yes." The station master paused and continued. "Somebody's coming over from the village." He nodded in the direction of a bowed figure stumbling through the blizzard and thick snow in the direction of the waiting-room down the platform. "Looks like Joe Black."

A flurry of snow blew into the cabin as the figure entered and asked, "Have you any news from Doctor Earnshaw, station master?"

"They'll be leaving Robin Hood's Bay soon Joe." replied the station master.

"Hope they open the road all the way to Castlebrough. Eileen's very ill, I'm scared for her. She's had four bairns before an' never had this long in labour. I think she'll need the hospital." Joe Black exhibited his worry. The signalling apparatus clanked out a message from Robin Hood's Bay. "He's asking for the tablet. Shouldn't be long now. Twenty minutes I'd say if he's leaving now," chattered Mr Welburn the station master as he operated the electrical equipment which released the tablet to allow the snowploughs leave Robin Hood's Bay and travel up the steep single line to Ravenscar.

★ ★ ★ ★

"How's yours steaming now Joe?" asked Frank Sutton, fireman on the G5 loco that was the second engine of the snowplough train at Robin Hood's Bay.

"Clapped out. Doesn't steam like it should. We should be alright up the bank if I start with a full boiler and a full head of steam." Joe banged his freezing arms across his body. "I don't want to be stopping at the brickyard for a blow-up in this weather."

"I've got some good coal," offered Frank. "Good shiny lumps of Yorkshire Main. I could spare you a few lumps if that'd help you."

"Sounds like a good idea. My tender's full of wet slack, teks a bit of burning," replied Joe. "Let's get a station barrow and I'll have a few lumps." Frank Sutton was mating a Malton driver on the G5 side tank loco. He advised his driver, "I'm just going to give my pal a few good lumps of Yorkshire Main to help him keep steam. It's a crap J21 an' he's got a load of wet slack in the tender."

"Okay but don't give him too much, these engines only have small bunkers. We'll move up when Ted is ready and fill our tank before leaving, then we're safe if we get held up. Turn your injector off." Frank obliged his driver, closed the water injector and turned to hand lumps of coal out through the doorway to Joe Wade but a noisy rush of steam told him that the injector clack had stuck in open position. A jet of steam was loudly escaping from the injector water-overflow pipe beneath the engine.

"Bang that clackbox with a spanner mate and see if that'll seat it," Frank's driver instructed. The trouble persisted. He restarted the

injector a number of times, but each time the clack valve would not
re-seat and they had to leave it loudly wasting steam down the side of
the engine.

"That'll make it harder for us to make a full head of steam all the
time," Frank grumbled as they transferred a quantity of coal to a
station barrow for Joe's tall-chimneyed tender engine. "These Jays are
good engines up this road, nearly as good as the 'Whitby Willies' and
the A8's."

Joe nodded in partial agreement, "Would be if they had larger
fireboxes. A bit on the small side for a lot of work. They keep their
feet well up this road. That's in their favour."

All available hands at Robin Hood's Bay were using shovels
and scrapers to remove snow and ice to get the station back to full
working order following the overnight heavy snow. The station
master brought the tablet to Joe's driver, Ted Coney, and then
introduced Doctor Earnshaw to Joe and Ted. "This is the Doc I told
you about. He's got to get to the peak as soon as you can get him
there. There's a lady up there needs a doctor badly." He laughed at his
slack speech. "Badly needs a doctor I think I mean."

"Where are you going to ride Doctor?" asked Joe who had just
finished moving the coal.

"I've always fancied a ride on a locomotive."

"So have lots of people. It's rather mucky, even a bit risky for a
passenger," reminded Big Ted Coney the Malton driver who was Joe
Wade's driver-mate for the day. Big Ted was a giant figure in the
confines of the medium sized sheeted cab of the J21. He towered
nearly six-feet and had a body and limbs that put him around sixteen
stone. His almost bald head carried a large floppy civvy cloth cap.
When Joe met him he wondered how the man entered the cab through
the narrow doors.

"There'll be room in the snow vans with the men. There'll be a cup
o' tea, too," explained the station master and walked off towards the
first plough followed by the doctor. The gang were stacking their tools
and occupying their places in the two boxploughs which each faced
their snowplough blades in opposite directions. The two locos were
marshalled tender-to-tender between the boxploughs. Which ever
direction the coupled ploughs progressed the leading loco was always
front-end on into the snow and the rear loco was travelling in reverse.

The station master and Joe accompanied the doctor to the first van.
Joe was merely curious, he'd never been inside a railway boxplough.
The dark van interior exuded heat from a glowing hot coal stove and
clouds of cigarette and pipe smoke drifted idly around the van

catching the shafts of light from the paraffin lamps and the small dirty windows. Tea and dominoes awaited the men. The fixed table and forms down the centre for about eight men were being noisily occupied.

"I can't stand all that smoke. I'll be oiking and spewing after five minutes," rebelled the doctor. "It stinks as well."

"The other van will be just the same."

"Not suitable for a country gentleman," returned the doctor. Joe couldn't help the thought registering; 'He hardly talks like a country gentleman. More like a product of the soil, bubbling and rough, almost earthy'.

"I'll travel with the driver."

"It'll be filthy on there. Look at this fireman," advised the station master. Joe's appearance demonstrated the point even though he wore his overcoat and balaclava and displayed only his hands and acne spotted face.

"Don't you take passengers on the footplate? I've seen more than two men on sometimes." The doctor addressed his question to Joe.

"Well, er yes, but you should have a pass, a footplate pass from someone. Anyway, ask the driver."

"I haven't got a pass. I've got a pound, and a flask of rum. Anyway I ain't travelling in the van. It stinks like a dry privy. I've seen better cattle wagons." The doctor turned away in the direction of Joe's leading locomotive as the guard shouted in the direction of the two locos, "I'm ready if you are?". The doctor took the handrails of the J21 and hauled himself aboard brushing his full figure against the tender and the cab side.

"You'll ruin your suit, Doctor," advised the station master. "I've got a long railway mackintosh in the office. I'll fetch it." He made off without waiting for an answer.

The safety valves of the two engines were simmering away, indicating that each had a full head ready for the 'off'. The sharp jet of escaping steam from the sticking injector clack announced the waste of valuable steam.

"I'm travelling with you driver. There isn't room for a cat in that van," announced the doctor and then added, "And I've got a heart warmer for you, it'll warm the cockles of your heart. Unless you've signed the pledge and you are on the wagon."

"Do I look as if I've signed the pledge?" asked Driver Coney with a grin and a pat on his larger than usual belly. He took the offered flask of rum and poured a small quantity into the lid of his billy can. He savoured it slowly. "You a doctor, are you? Going to Ravenscar?"

"Yes, there's a young woman in labour and she's in trouble. Needs a doctor and I'm the only one available. Couldn't make it in my car. Can't get it out of Robin Hood's Bay."

"There's the whistle, son," the driver said to Joe and then looked out down the platform. "We're off!" he called out at the sight of the guard's waving flag. "Eleven a.m." he commented with a glance at his watch as he released the engine Westinghouse brake with a blast of compressed air. The two engine whistles popped and the regulators opened up and moved the full train into life.

"Sit on my seat, Doctor," instructed Joe. "You'll keep cleaner then." He held the old mackintosh for the doctor to pull on his back. "No thanks," he said to the doctor's offer of a drop from the flask. "My guts are upset with getting up early this morning."

"You an early riser then?"

"Only on early turns. I sleep in on late turns."

"What about today?"

"I was early preparation and station pilot, 4 a.m. Should have been finished for 12 noon but this snow disrupted early morning workings into Castlebrough and I was changed to crew the snowploughs that Ted brought in from York."

"You live in Castlebrough, do you?"

"Yes." He picked up his firing shovel. "I'd better start on this old crab, she's not steaming well," concluded Joe as the two engines and the two ploughs rolled noisily into life.

The line gradients fell for a while as the ploughs left Robin Hood's Bay station for Ravenscar and made a good start possible. Drifted snow threatened to halt their progress every time they met a dip in the line and terrain, but the combined efforts of the J21 loco and the smaller G5 overcame all the snow obstructing their path. The ninety-feet high embankment over Stoupe Beck, which they crossed, was free of snow and gave them a good run towards Fyling Hall where the real work of climbing up to Ravenscar peak commenced.

The rail route to the top was becoming visible from the locomotives despite the blizzard; it wound up the steep bank to the right and enabled a hazy view of the rolling North Sea to the left. The falling snow had almost ceased and the sky had lightened making horizons slightly visible. The majestic falling terrain rolled down to the sea and much of its rugged landscape and occasional farm buildings broke through the heavy white blanket. Whittaker's non-working brickyard with its ruined kilns, rail sidings and tall brick chimneys revealed how man's hand had marked the moors over many years. The line was unique because of its steep, three mile gradient of

1 in 39. Joe loved this climb. There was something brave and inspiring about its journey through the steep falling moorland in close proximity to the coast of Yorkshire. Joe loved the free-wheeling run from Ravenscar down to Fyling Hall and Robin Hood's Bay, he felt he communed with nature and became poetic and lyrical about this wild moorland escarpment with its carefully carved out farms.

The respite from the falling snow was not to last for long. The turbulent stratospheric winds saw to that, they rolled thick snow clouds landwards and soon driving snow replaced the gently falling flakes.

"Yuh keepin' her end up are you son? Hope so 'cos the G5 behind isn't doing so well," Ted Coney commented to Joe, who was struggling to maintain a full steam pressure of 170 pounds in the boiler of the J21.

"Only because I've sacrificed the water level. As soon as I put the water injector on the pressure falls. She don't steam, Ted. Got a perfect fire on too."

"The G5 won't be steaming well with that clack blowing like hell," commented Ted Coney. "We'll stop for a blow-up before we get too far into the bank." After a pause he added, "There's a bit of straight track up ahead. I think we'll get started easily enough." He alerted the other engine crew with three quick blasts on his whistle and closed his regulator. For ten minutes they halted, raised steam and filled the boiler whilst the snow-gang cleared the snow from the tracks in front for as far as they could. Joe visited Frank Sutton and learnt that he too was having difficulties with steam pressure, but in his case it was the injector clack refusing to seat and make a steam-tight boiler.

Doctor Earnshaw, thrilled by his footplate journey, expressed concern about the time it was taking him to attend his patient, "I hope Mrs Black is holding on alright, it's nearly an hour since I got the call for help."

"We'll be another fifteen minutes before we get to the top," Ted assured him. "We can go as soon as the gang get aboard."

With the two engines refreshed and with sand pipes sanding the rails, they struggled noisily towards the summit and the tunnel. Ted Coney was putting full effort into the cylinders of his six driving-wheeled locomotive, loud clear blasts ripped away from the chimney top as the fully opened regulator allowed full boiler pressure into the two cylinders of the old J21. Joe fired slowly with all the care and art he could muster. His shovel, carrying small amounts of the fine wet coal-slack, cut a careful arc from the coal bunker to the firehole door. He fired with the hanging flapper door in closed position, his shovel struck the hanging door plate at speed and shot the coal to its predestined spot on the firebed and then the hanging door fell shut. He wanted to make a good job of being a fireman especially today because he would qualify as a first year fireman on the completion of today's shift. He would henceforth always get a fireman's pay, even when there were no firing duties for him, unless of course he was demoted for disciplinary reasons. He paused only to keep an eye on the discolouration of the exhaust at the chimney head and to occasionally view the white-hot firebed down his shovel blade.

★ ★ ★ ★

2
WHEN THE BOILER BLEW.

Slowly the two locos devoured the yards to the summit, their wheels gripped the rails without the help of the sanding mechanism. 'If you'd only steam, damn you,' Joe spoke silently to his loco, 'We'd be alright, but we're losing water level rapidly.'

"Are we stopping for another blow-up at the brickyard, Ted?" Joe asked. "I can't put any water in the boiler without the boiler pressure falling." Joe wasn't confident that they would make it through the tunnel if they didn't stop for steam.

"No we're not stopping. We're going to need all the speed we can muster to get through that tunnel. The cutting at the end will be full of snow." Ted looked at the water level in the boiler-gauge glasses. They displayed about two inches of water. "Don't put your injector on yet."

Joe was uneasy. Outside of the sheeted engine cab the wind howled with renewed vigour and the driving snow lost its soft fluffy nature and cut through the air like driven ice. The doctor kept his head out, acting as look-out while Joe laboured with his small amounts of slack coal. Joe joined the doctor for a few moments and shared his concern about the lowering level of water in the boiler. "It shows just over an inch of water in the glass," Joe explained to Doctor Earnshaw, "but we're going uphill, which means that most of the water lies at this end of the boiler. If we suddenly levelled out we'd be lucky to have any water in sight."

"How does that matter?" asked the doctor.

"If the firebox top was bare of water, uncovered, for just an instant the firebox lead plugs would blow out."

"What'd happen then."

"I've no idea. I've never seen it happen. It'd be like the boiler getting a couple of holes in it."

"It wouldn't blow up, would it. Like in 'where was the engine driver when the boiler blew up'."

"No, the lead plugs are a safety device to stop that happening," concluded Joe and turned the water injector on without recourse to his driver. He didn't like to see the water level about to disappear. Ted kept his head out into the storm and Joe coaxed his fire. The steam pressure fell slowly to just less than one hundred and fifty pounds per square inch. Suddenly Ted left his engine controls and stepped across the cab and closed down the water injector. "We'll have to risk it or we'll never get through. Leave it off 'til we clear the tunnel and the cutting at the other end." He turned back to Joe, "Put a pricker through the fire and burn off the smoke before we enter the tunnel."

"How long is the tunnel, son?" asked the doctor.

"About a quarter of a mile, but it isn't straight, it bends a bit and causes slipping." He lit his water column gauge lamp so he could keep an eye on the disappearing water level when they were in the blackness of the tunnel. He pushed the long fire iron through the fire and redistributed it evenly. He was satisfied with its condition.

The cutting at the tunnel mouth had accumulated considerable drifting snow. The front plough cut into it and threw snow to each side, some of it to fall back into the wheels of the following engines. The regulator was wide open, the wheels were gripping the rails, there was nothing more that Ted or Joe could do. They struck the tunnel mouth with a suddenness that surprised Joe and the doctor, the subdued light of the middle day vanished suddenly from the cab and cascading frozen snow showered on the engine and found its way through the cab roof vent and into each side of the cab.

The doctor ducked involuntarily as snow showered his head and lap, he almost fell from the fireman's seat in his haste to avoid the deluge. Ted ducked also as he suffered the same fate on the other side of the cab, Joe, shook from his shoulders the small amount that had struck him. The anti-glare tarpaulin sheet caught a weight of snow that would otherwise have entered the cab. Joe's concern was the absence of a water level in his gauge glasses and the one hundred and forty pounds of steam pressure in his boiler. He really should put the water injector on.

"Ted, I'll have to put the water on, it's out of sight."

"Not yet, you'll stop us if you do."

The shiny black wet walls of the tunnel crept painfully past the cab sides, the exhausts of the two engines blasted from the chimneys and exploded on the tunnel roof and a torrent of noise flooded their ears. Joe couldn't see his engine chimney through the cab spectacle windows because of impacted snow but he could visualise it shooting hot coals into the tunnel's black interior.

"She's keeping her feet, that's one good thing. If we start slipping we'll be stuck inside, probably snowed up at either end too," Joe told the doctor and added, "if the steam pressure drops much more the vacuum brakes'll start to go on and stop us." He stepped across the cab and shouted in Ted's ear. "I'll have to put the injector on Ted, can't see any water."

"Put it on a fine setting," replied Ted. Joe lost no time and was pleased to hear the injector successfully singing away. "Can't be far

now," yelled Ted with an eye on the falling pressure needle. The black
wet tunnel walls, catching the firelight, slid by and Joe peppered his
fire with the best coal he could find. The doctor stood on the tender
fall-plate close by Joe, and the driver used his large vacuum ejector to
keep the vacuum brake system working. Everything seemed to add to
the clamour of noise. The sudden impact took them by surprise and
threw the three men towards the boiler, the weight of the train pressed
on breaking through its initial contact with snow.

The blackness of the tunnel abruptly gave way to a flurry of
daylight and flying snow as the plough broke through the deep drift
at the exit of the tunnel. Snow fell into the cab and sprayed the crew
and their passenger. The engine whistle screeched its warning as the
plough and the engines burst out and fought with the snow. Joe
adjusted his injector to feed more water into the depleted boiler as
the pressure ducked to one hundred pounds. They struggled
forwards and upwards through the two hundred yard long snow
blocked cutting. Joe caught sight of the first semaphore signal
post with its drooping red board admitting them forward into
Ravenscar's two-platformed railway station. The snow storm still
raged and bowed the two platelayer figures who were clear of the
track and on the sloping sides of the cutting.

"We're nearly there now Doc," shouted Ted jubilantly across the
steamy coal-strewn cab, "Just a bit more effort and we're high and
dry." Ted looked at the empty gauge glasses and dropped his eyes to
the water injector controls and noted that the right-hand injector was
propelling water into the depleted boiler. He was having difficulty
maintaining his necessary twenty-one inches of vacuum in the train
brake pipe. It was quite obvious that the accompanying G5 loco
didn't have enough steam to make the vacuum brake system work
more effectively. "C'mon me ole beauty," he urged, "let's mek it
into the station."

Only a few yards stood between them and the level track. Joe
moved to the left side of the cab and started the other water injector
and then stepped across to the doctor who stood close to the cab
doorway. "We've made it Doctor. Bin close but we've made it. The
snow's deep here."

No words of reply left the doctor's whiskered lips, he was looking
in the direction of Ted Coney who reached to close the regulator and
let the deep snow halt the forward motion of the the two locos and
ploughs. The engine halted as if the brakes had been applied and in
that instant a steam jet screamed a warning. During that brief instant
Joe recorded the unexpected thought that his engine safety valves

were blowing off steam. Then he knew they weren't, the blasting commotion was in the engine firebox, steam and hot fire were expelled back through the fire door into the cab. Joe heaved on the bulky figure of the doctor standing between him and the cab doorway, "Get out! Get out! quick." He pushed so violently that the doctor was catapulted headlong into the snow. Joe's last vision of the cab filling with steam and hot dust was of Ted Coney's body and legs disappearing headlong through the driver's window. Joe toppled into the snow and on top of the doctor, his wits were recollected as he realised hot water from the injector water overflow pipe was flowing onto his feet and legs.

"What happened?" asked the winded Doctor Earnshaw as he floundered in the snow beneath Joe.

"Lord knows. Summat's bust. Like a steam pipe in the firebox." He struggled to upright himself and then the awful truth settled into his consciousness at a high anxiety level, the lead plugs had fused. He felt a surge of panic at the thought that 'the boiler must have been empty and the lead plugs had blown out to save the boiler from blowing up.' He scrambled upright in the three feet of snow and looked up to his wounded loco. The cab was filled with steam which was blowing out to add to the turbulence of the blizzard. He stumbled back towards the G5 locomotive and climbed into the cab.

"What's happened?" asked Frank as their eyes met.

"We must have dropped our lead plugs."

"Bloody hell! That's serious if you have, you can't have."

"Where's my mate?" asked Joe and crossed over the cab and looked down the platform. Ted was struggling to his feet with the aid of the G5 driver, he'd emerged from the cab window head first at great speed and landed on his shoulder and head on the platform which fortunately was covered in the thick snow thrown back by the plough.

"The plugs have gone," Ted said simply to the G5 driver as if he was stating that he'd just missed a train connection.

"Can't get in the cab yet mate. Do you think your mate's still in there?"

"No," said Ted as calmly as before. "He's coming down the platform from your engine." Ted Coney had picked himself up as Joe stumbled towards him through the deep snow. "Where's the doctor?" Ted asked with his first show of concern.

"He's on the snow at the other side. He fell out of the cab, onto the snow. I think he's alright." Joe answered.

"Go and help him."

Joe obeyed without a murmur. The roar of escaping steam was diminishing but the cab was still inhospitable and the two water injectors had ceased working as the steam pressure had fallen. When Joe joined the doctor, two gangers from the plough were helping him to his feet and guiding him unsteadily to the platform through the deep snow. They lifted him bodily from the track onto the platform edge and then ushered and dragged him towards the signal cabin.

"What's happened?" asked two or three voices. "Is he alright?"

"He needs a doctor. Course, he is a doctor," said the station master as his mind caught up with what his mouth was saying.

The doctor steadied himself in the wooden chair in which he had been seated and then applied his own medicine. His flask of rum brought him around and alerted him to Ted Coney's own needs. "Here Ted. You know what to do with this." Ted didn't need any persuading but neither he nor the doctor thought about Joe.

"What happened then?" asked the station master.

"We've broken down." Ted Coney said with a surprising lack of emotion.

"Can't you repair it?" asked the station master innocently.

The question went unheeded as the doctor recovered. "My bag! Where is it?" Then he answered his own question. "It's on the floor in front of where I was sat on the engine."

"It's down the side of the boiler just in front of the fireman's seat," affirmed Joe.

"It'll be ruined by that steam and water. It's got my equipment in." He rose shakily to his feet and made to go towards the door. "I've got to see Mrs Black."

"Sit there Doc. We'll go and look for your bag. Come on son." Big Ted rolled passively into action, caught Joe by the arm, and expressed his intention to find the doctor's bag.

The cab of the J21 locomotive was the centre of attraction to the snow gang and a few other railmen in spite of the raging blizzard. They observed the soaked and dirt strewn interior of the cab, steam still sizzled and blew from the firebox opening and obscured clear observation of the interior.

"Move over mates. Let the dog see the rabbit." Ted Coney shouldered his way through the onlookers and Joe followed in his wake. Together they climbed into the cab of their locomotive and viewed the desolation, not at any danger from the steam clouds slowly emerging from the firebox.

"In that corner Ted," offered Joe. But the advice wasn't required. Ted reached down into the steamy corner of the cab and emerged with the strong leather medical bag. Apart from filth and heavy condensation it appeared to be little harmed. "Unless," muttered Joe, "the contents are damaged." The doctor confirmed that all was in order.

"More than we can say about our little lot," Ted Coney imparted to Joe in a quiet voice as they saw the doctor depart through the falling snow to number three Railway Cottages with the female figure who had come to meet him. "Let's look at the damage to our little chariot, as if we didn't know."

Joe became aware of growing anxiety as he realised the magnitude of their calamity. He was the fireman and he'd just run out of steam and water and had blown the plugs on his locomotive. 'Good God! That was a blinking big error'. He corrected the thoughts that were emerging. 'That's a bloody understatement. It's a bloody disaster'. They were stranded on the six-hundred feet high peak on the Yorkshire Moors in severe winter conditions only a few hundred yards from the North Sea with a locomotive that didn't work. He didn't dare start a discussion on 'What went wrong?' He feared the answer that 'The fireman let the boiler water level fall so far that the fusible plugs in the firebox blew'.

"Are you ready, Ted, to shunt your engine into the yard?" asked the G5 driver. "It isn't going to go anywhere."

"When the gang clear enough snow to let us begin some movements," Ted replied, "We'll uncouple the last plough and push it back down the line to the tunnel and leave it, then you push us into the goods siding." To Joe he said, "Keep the tablet. Don't surrender it to the station master. That'll protect us from a train coming up from Robin Hood's Bay."

"Nowt'll come up that line today," said Frank Sutton and then decided quickly to keep his mouth shut in the sensitive situation.

"The tablet's still hanging on the handbrake of our engine," offered Joe.

"Cab's in a mess," continued Ted to Joe, still refusing to pass any comment on what went wrong. Joe noted that omission with some relief although he knew that he'd never avoid the inevitable inquest as long as he lived. The day of reckoning would dawn. "Put our gear on the G5. Move everything that might go missing while the engine's up here. It'll be a while before they'll shift it. Better start on the fire if you can get near. Mek sure that it's dead. If it's burning get it out. For safety's sake chuck it all out as soon as you can get near to it with your shovels."

Joe obliged without comment despite the cold and the snow. There weren't going to be any more mistakes. He made sure the tablet stayed with him until Ted came to take it to the G5 driver. He threw all the remaining clinker and fire out from the firebox, turned every handle and valve to closed position and made sure the injector overflow pipes were not leaking water that would freeze and cause damage. He even cleaned the cab as if he could erase all sign of the tragedy that was going to blight his railway reputation for the rest of his life. One thing he found very hard to do was to end the constant debate in his mind about whose fault it was. It wasn't his fault. Ted had told him to turn the water off and not to put it on until they got through the snow and the tunnel. But, who was the fireman? Whose responsibility was it to maintain steam and a safe level of water in the boiler? Joe tried to avoid the answers.

The dead J21 was shunted into the goods siding, then the G5 marshalled itself between the two ploughs and swept the line to the tunnel and every part of the station. Joe and Ted surrendered the tablet as soon as the ploughs had left the tunnel and the cutting and they stowed their gear in the lockers of the G5 locomotive. Ted Coney hoped to travel on the snowplough to Castlebrough and then go to Malton where he privately expected to be disciplined for the loss of his locomotive. Joe kept quiet and never raised the subject of what would happen to him. His only question was, "Where can I get something to eat? There are some shops in the station square. Must be a food shop somewhere in a village of this size."

"Do you like rabbit stew?" the station master asked Joe and Ted.

"Where would we get rabbit stew?" Joe answered the question with another. But Ted had other ideas. "Yes," was his definite response.

"My wife's got some on the stove, and some spuds and bread. You look as though you could do with a wash Joe, dry your boots and trousers. There's a fire and hot water in our wash-house. Show him to our house Ralph. Ask my missus to help him tidy up. What's wrong with your hand son?"

"Just a bit of a burn, something hot from the firebox hit my hand when the plugs burst. Just a little burn," he said displaying the small burnt area on the back of his hand.

"Ask Mrs Fisher to bind it up for you," instructed Station Master Fisher as Joe went off with Ralph. "Come back to the signal cabin for your food."

★ ★ ★ ★

3
Who Holds the Baby?

Number Three Railway Cottages was steamy, busy and noisy. An ancient brick, coal-fired water-boiler crackled and boiled in the corner of the stone-flagged scullery and the snowy outdoor scene was visible through the small-paned window that poured light into the primitive room. Doctor Earnshaw was washing his hands and scalding some implements in an enamel bowl. An ancient wrinkled female neighbour, in the front living-room, minded the ten-year old daughter, who pretended to be cleaning with a brush and dust pan.

"The baby alright Doctor?" called the old lady. "Can I go up then?"

"Mrs Black's not out of trouble yet," he started. After a brief pause he asked, "Could you get someone to go over for the station master? Don't you go, or the youngster. Can you get a neighbour to go?"

"One of the neighbours is upstairs with you. Do you want her to go?"

"No dear, I need both the ladies. You can find someone to go, can't you?"

"Sure Doctor. I'll go for Mrs Chantrey. She'll make it through the snow to the station. It's not falling so fast now. What do you want her to say?"

"I want the station master over here as soon as you can get him. I'm wanted upstairs. Be a good woman. Send someone over as quickly as you can." He was interrupted from upstairs with the call of "Doctor, can you come? Hurry please."

On the landing in the bedroom doorway one of the women helpers addressed him. "She's having another one, Doctor, we think." The bedroom scene confirmed the news for the doctor. On the rude bed, Mrs Black, moaning and displaying a very weak physical condition, lay exposed with a second child emerging into life.

"This one's breech. One of you see to the baby girl. You, Mrs Smith help me. Take these." He offered the surgical tools to Mrs Smith and attended to the weakly straining Mrs Black. "Now," he called, "Push my dear it will soon be over. That's the buttocks." As Doctor Earnshaw viewed the flaccid body and limbs of the tiny boy he controlled his anxiety and encouraged Mrs Black. "Come on dear just the head. There we have him. There little fellow. A boy - a brother for your little girl." He paused in his encouragements to concentrate on the technicalities of the birth; the little fellow squalled at the shock of birth and wriggled as the doctor severed him from his umbilical dependency. "You are a little fellow - at the side of your sister. Get you in a pint pot, we could. There, what do you say about that. A bit cleaner now. Come on little chap, look at your Mam." A chorus of chat and baby talk came from the doctor and the lady helpers. The mother smiled weakly as they displayed her tiny son before her vision.

"We are going to try and get you to hospital, Mrs Black. You've lost a lot of blood. You need a transfusion. And the little fellow is, well, very frail, he needs to be in hospital with you. What shall we call the little chap? Eh?"

"She's got five girls now, and this little fellow," added one of the helpers. "What do think, Mary?" she asked the pallid and silent mother. "You've got a little Joey here, looks the spitten image of his Dad. The mother smiled feebly and uttered, "Little Joe. Joe will like that."

"Where is Mr Black now?" asked the helper Daisy Mason.

The other helper chose to answer the question for Mary Black. "He's on afternoons at the station. I'll go and fetch him now. You can manage while I go can't you Daisy?" said Daisy Mason's helper and friend and continued. "Sounds like the station master has called to see you, Doctor." Her gestures indicated that she'd heard and recognised the voice that had just drifted up the stairs.

"You've got a little brother now as well as a little sister," said Doctor Earnshaw to the ten year old daughter who waited excitedly at the foot of the stairs. The station master and a uniformed porter were in the plainly furnished living room in answer to Doctor Earnshaw's call.

"She's had two?" gabbled Joe Black. "Lord, I only had four when I went to work, now I've got six."

"You'll have to tie a knot in it now, that's certain. Goin' to bed early that's what does it."

"Er sherup Gran. What do you know about it?"

"I know this, if they'd taken you into the army and sent you to the desert you'd still only have three. There's eight mouths for you to feed now Joe. You'll have to quarter them two eggs you all share at breakfast. I'm disgusted, you're not even a Catholic family."

"How's our lass Doctor? That's what I want to know."

"That's what I wanted to see the station master about," said the doctor by the way of answering Joe Black's question. "We've got to get her and the two babies to hospital. It's urgent, your Mary needs a blood transfusion. Little Joey needs an oxygen tent and delicate care for a week or two."

"That's not going to be easy in this weather. We'll have to get the emergency services out," added the station master. "I'll go and see what I can do. You'd better stay here Joe, take the rest of the day off. You'll need it after what you've just gone through."

★ ★ ★ ★

"Reet good rabbit stew," Joe Wade smacked his lips. "Can't beat a good rabbit off the moors." He looked more presentable now in fresh large-fitting, dry trousers and without his fingerless mittens and the close fitting balaclava, his face and hands were in a state of moderate cleanliness. He toasted large-fitting old slippers on his feet in front of a glowing coal stove in the station signal cabin at Ravenscar. His tragedy with the engine plugs had slipped down his scale of importance, it had hardly featured in the discussions that had occupied the four locomen as they devoured the rabbit stew and bread provided by the station master's wife.

"I've got to find a way of getting Mrs Black and her bairns to hospital," announced the station master as he arrived back in the cabin. "It's a good job the snow's stopped. I've been talking to the emergency services and to traffic control. The roads from Castlebrough, especially from Cloughton are under deep drifts and the line to Castlebrough is blocked by heavy drifts at Stainton Dale but if we could get the ploughs through to Cloughton with Mrs Black on board they could pick her up with the ambulance and get her to Castlebrough Hospital."

"What's the roads like out of Whitby?" asked the G5 driver.

"Blocked solid. They block easily with drifting snow when the wind's off the sea."

"What about coast guard service? Or the Observer Corps in Raven Hall?" asked Frank Sutton.

"No luck from them either, but they might come back with something," replied the station master.

"Where's the doctor?" asked Big Ted.

"He's up at the church hall with the A.R.P. locals. Fitting up a stretcher and covers in case we have to move Mrs Black down to the station."

"What will they bring her here for?"

"He's hoping we may be able to use the ploughs to get down to Cloughton. I told him it's nearly all down hill to Stainton Dale and Cloughton and the ploughs might get through."

"Did you tell him that we only have half a loco?" asked the G5 driver.

"You've got yours. What's wrong with that?"

"We've got a clack blowing on the right-hand injector. It's blowing bad. Affects her steaming. We had two locos on the way up. Now there's only mine."

"She'll move," responded the station master. "You've been sweeping the station since you've been on your own."

"But that's not the same as running at speed with the two ploughs on," added the driver.

"Yes, but down hill if you've got to."

"I doubt we'd mek it."

"It's our only option. Joe thinks you'll take her and the bairns, if all else fails."

"What me?" blurted out Joe Wade.

"No, not you. Joe Black, the father," said the station master a little irritably. "It might be life or death."

"It'd be easier to go back to Whitby," added Joe Wade. "We've swept that line on the way up. Course that'd be no good to me and Frank. We've got to get back to Castlebrough. It makes more sense for us if the ploughs try to make it through to Cloughton and then to Castlebrough." Joe's suggestion about Whitby seemed to go unnoticed until the doctor arrived in the cabin.

"I want you to try and get her and the bairns down to Cloughton and on to Castlebrough General as fast as you can," said Doctor Earnshaw.

"We'd have a job to mek it with just our loco in the state she's in. Be a different matter if the J21 hadn't dropped its plugs." The G5 driver's remark burnt deep into Joe and generated a guilt complex.

"What's the matter with Whitby, Doctor?" chipped in big Ted. "There's a hospital there."

"There's the West Cliff hospital. But all the roads to Whitby are blocked worse than to Castlebrough," replied Doctor Earnshaw.

"You'd get the ploughs through to Whitby, wouldn't you Jack?" Ted Coney sought the approval of the G5 driver.

"Reckon so. We've just come up that way. Cleared Robin Hood's Bay station an' all. We could get water there too."

"It's nearly all falling ground. Damn sure you'd get through. Could get another loco at Whitby shed too, I bet," responded Ted with a little uncharacteristic enthusiasm. "And make your way back over Goathland summit to Pickering and get us two back to Malton."

"That sounds like what I want, station master," said the doctor. "We can get the stretcher in one plough and all the gang in the other, can't we?" The doctor's statement and question brought a new enthusiasm to the discussion.

"We want to get to Castlebrough, don't we Joe?" stated Frank Sutton.

"That's alright son," answered Ted. "Jack will fire to me. That's how we started out today, didn't we Jack?"

"The plough cabins will be full if you're taking the lady and the bairns in one cabin. You'll need privacy for the doctor and the lady," contributed Blaster Baines the ganger.

"Let's get the job done. I'll get the plough lads to bring the babies and Mrs Black." Doctor Earnshaw sounded impatient. "We'll have to fix the stretcher on the table in the plough. I want those two ladies who helped at the birth to come with me. Can't really have strange men around Mrs Black. She's real ill. Will want some privacy. Hope we're going to be in time, There's six kids and a man in her life."

"Can I come with you Doctor?" asked Joe Black, the husband, who'd been a silent witness to the discussion.

"What about your four children? Don't you think they are going to need you?" questioned the doctor as they moved out of the signal cabin. "There isn't going to be room."

"What about us?" asked Frank Sutton of Joe Wade. "We've got to eat and sleep and get back home. You tell em Joe. You can be mouthy when you want to be."

There wasn't the chance for Joe to protest. Anyway he didn't feel a bit mouthy. The snow had ceased and the north-easterly wind had subsided slightly. Frank and Joe helped bring Mary Black and her new born twins from the cottage and bind the stretcher to the table. The occupied plough-cabin offered security and warmth and an amazing quantity of domestic provisions, utensils, tools and clothes. The hot coal-fired stove and the large simmering kettle made for a secure refuge. Frank and Joe felt cheated as they watched the small G5, between the two snowploughs, leave the platform and approach the cutting on the line to the tunnel where Joe had experienced the disaster of a blown boiler. The snowdrifts with the vertical sides created earlier by the passage of the ploughs swallowed them and then gave them up to the tunnel mouth. Few figures stood around now. The only sign of the drama on the peak was Joe's cold, lifeless, now snow-covered, J21 locomotive in the siding alongside the line to Whitby.

★ ★ ★ ★

4
It's Snow Excuse.

Joe and Frank settled down in the station waiting-room. Darkness established itself early but bed-time was far away. They sat in two rough chairs close to the roaring hot stove in the centre. A straw palliasse awaited them on the floor and two paraffin lamps provided light enough for reading.

"This is better than splitting up and taking digs in two separate houses. There'd o' been no peace for me in my billet with all those kids. Don't know where I'd've slept. Didn't ask to see the bedroom. You saved me Joe when you said we can sleep in the waiting-room."

Joe used the private time they had available to reveal his worries and tell Frank how his engine had blown its fusible plugs. "I was carrying out Ted Coney's instruction not to put the injector on."

"You were the fireman Joe. They'll say you were responsible."

"Bloody hell! Do you think I'll be finished?"

Frank just shook his head sideways slowly.

"Do you know what'll happen next?" Joe questioned Frank. "I'll have to make out a report, I know that. Do you think there'll be a 'Form One' for me, or a 'Caution'? They can do worse than that, can't they? Wonder if they ever sack anyone for dropping the plugs. God, it's a big job putting a firebox back in order."

"Let's hope it's not buckled. If they have to fit a new firebox, that'll cost the bloody earth. Might even scrap the engine," went on Frank pessimistically.

"You're bloody well enjoying this aren't yuh Frank? Call yourself a mate!"

"Not really, just preparing yuh for the worst. The unions'll represent yuh Joe. You'll be alright."

"I'm not likely to forget all this. Or sleep tonight."

"Go and borrow some more sacks and carpets if you're not yet comfortable."

"I'm not sleeping yet daft beggar," Joe replied with mock anger. "I'm thinking of finding a place where we can get a drink or talk to somebody. The station master's wife told us to go in for a bite of supper at nine but I don't really feel like bothering her."

"Let's go up to that church hall that the A.R.P. use. Sure to be someone there. The roadway was clear enough when they brought the stretcher down."

The night was now almost friendly, stars twinkled in the canopy of the night. Amazingly the dark snow clouds of earlier had vanished and the cutting winds were subdued to a mere, unfriendly breeze.

"We could call in to the cabin and see how Mrs Black and the Doctor fared. Like to know where Big Ted and Jack are," added Joe. "They needn't have left us up here."

The mother and child were in West Cliff Hospital. The news looked good. Ted and Jack were on their way up to the Goathland summit from Whitby with another Whitby G5 engine replacing theirs. They were on their way home to Malton. The line over Goathland summit was open and passenger services were resumed from Whitby to Pickering.

"It'll be tomorrow before we get home. I wonder why they left us Frank? They must have had an idea that they might get back to Malton that way. They don't have to worry about getting us back to Castlebrough."

"They needn't have left us," emphasised Frank. "Said they would pick us up on the way back. Yuh know what I think, Joe, Big Ted wants to get his report in first about the plugs being blown. It's a Castlebrough engine that's bust, not a Malton one. Sure as hell he'll be blaming you."

"You do make me cheerful, Frank." Joe changed the subject, "See that chink of light from the A.R.P. post, you'd think they'd be more careful than that. On a big headland too. Like a lighthouse to a German plane."

"Specially on a clear night like this," Frank agreed as they walked towards the village hall. "With all this snow, almost as light as day."

"There's nowt of interest happening here," said Frank as he creaked the door open. Two Womens Auxiliary Air Force privates were sampling a dark coloured bottled beer and three cigarette-smoking local farm hands rattled the inevitable dominoes. A Royal Observer Corps sergeant, helmets, maps, telephones and stirrup pumps illustrated the wartime use of the church hall.

Joe and Frank walked uninvited into the hall. They aroused no immediate curiosity until Frank said, "You're showing a light. Saw it all the way from the station."

"That'd be Joe Black. He's slipped home for a bottle of rum," said one of the domino school. With that Joe Black, still in his L.N.E.R uniform, entered and banged the door noisily.

"Pity we can't get down to the Flask Inn," Joe Black said. "We'll just have to wash the babies' heads in this Nesfield's mild and anoint 'em with a noggin o' this rum."

"Hi lads," a W.A.A.F. greeted Frank and Joe. "You need an

evening suit on to come in here. Or a wash at least."

"They can come in dressed as they like. Or undressed if they like," slurred and giggled Joe Black. "They're the lads that brought the Doc through from Robin Hood's Bay. Saved our lass, that did."

"You should be with your six kids," remonstrated the sergeant.

"Half o' the village is looking after them so's I can pickle me brain. That's what it's all for. I went to work with four mouths to feed and now I've got six. You'd want to pickle your brain. I'll remember January 24th 1945 as long as I live," he happily slurred on. "You two lads. Tell us about getting the doctor through here and what happened in the tunnel."

Joe had to oblige since Frank volunteered him to respond. Frank himself, true to form, avoided the limelight whilst pushing somebody else forward. Still, Joe was amazed at how he was able, quite unintentionally, to elaborate the story into a gallant rescue attempt undertaken at great personal risk to himself and the doctor. "When the boiler blew up, for that's really what happened when it blew its plugs, scalding steam and fire blew all over the bloody shop. Good job I had me overcoat on, and cap and balaclava. And me mittens. Only burn I got's this on the back of me hand," he demonstrated. "Got scalding hot water from my knees downwards."

"Lucky not to be in West Cliff Hospital with your Missus," added Frank to Joe Black as solemnly as he could. "Yes, I will have some more but this is the last. That'll do," he said. " No more. I'll split this with Joe. We're sleeping rough tonight. Haven't a bed. Don't want a bloody big head an' all."

"Haven't a bed! Why?" asked one of the W.A.A.F.s.

"Yuh going to offer him yours?" giggled Blaster Baines one of the locals.

"I'd rather sleep in the snow with him wi' nowt on than with you in bed with yer best suit on!" retorted the W.A.A.F. She repeated the question.

"I'll tell 'em, Joe," Frank said with a restraining arm on Joe's nearby hand - a sure sign to Joe that some variance of the truth was going to emerge. "We've been abandoned up here by our mates. They've bloody left us to get back to Castlebrough on our own."

"Why?" asked the W.A.A.F.s in unison.

"Cos there was only one engine and the driver wanted to get back to blow the whistle on Joe for the boiler plugs bursting. He wanted to get his pennyworth in before Joe got back home to tell his version," Frank added. Joe chose not to respond.

The next hour was filled with the usual wartime discussion; about the final rout of Von Runstedt's last desperate campaign, about the V2 rockets raining on Southern England in greater numbers, and the sudden surge in the German submarine offensive. Could the war really be coming to a close in 1945 when a savage winter in Europe and suicidal German resistance was hindering the Allies? The rugged, old local, Blaster Baines, had plenty of yarns to offer, about the railways, about his early years in the local quarries in the eighteen-hundreds, about the war and 'worse winters than this one'.

"Tide-time coming up. I'm going back to the post. You girls coming?" asked the sergeant. The girls and Joe and Frank trailed with him through the thick snow and the moonlit night. They called in to the station waiting-room where Frank and Joe were going to spend the night and sat around the stove talking, Blaster Baines joined them with his two labradors on a joint lead and conversation drifted on to local matters. Blaster liked to regale visitors with tales of the moors. He didn't know the sergeant very well and had only met Joe and Frank when they helped carry the stretcher so he knew they hadn't heard his yarns. Soon he was dominating the conversation.

"Soft as s-." He paused in deference to his two young female listeners. "Soft as slush, that's what railway workers are these days. Stop for the slightest bit of snow. We've had ten feet of snow up here in my time and kept the job running. No snowploughs or new fangled gadgets. Just muscle, little engines an' iron men. Don't know yus born. No unions, and crap like that. We doffed our caps to the Gentlemen of the estate and the station master. We knew our place, there was people who doffed their caps to us. Me Da' was the real Blaster up here. With his geli." He anticipated a question from Joe, "No, not the jelly and custard sort, the banging sort, gelignite. For blasting in the gannister quarries. He was like a watchmaker, so precise, could blast a two-ton rock to egg sizes with hardly any sweat. I was follering his trade but I blew me bloody toes off. They still calls me Blaster today, even though I'm more famous for blastin' me toes to the Almighty."

"Tell 'em about pushing the train full of passengers through the tunnel Blaster when the engine broke," egged on one of the W.A.A.F.s aware that Blaster had been started.

"Wi' pinch bars, hosses and muscle. Wouldn't let the Lord and his Lady and their guests get out of the train in the tunnel. Three coaches an' a seventy-five ton injun. In the dark, an' the smoke, an' the watter coming through the tunnel roof. Twenty on us and four hosses got the party of folks through the tunnel for the festivities at Raven Hal wi'out 'em being muckied. An' you lot think it's tough today."

"Tell 'em about the Mad Monarch and about the times he came to Raven Hall. George the Third you said," prompted the other W.A.A.F.

"Before my time. That was me old Granda's time, the Great-Granda's time really, just after t' Napoleonic Wars."

"But what about the smugglers from Robin Hood's Bay? Or the gamekeeper shooting?"

"It'll have to be without me," said the sergeant. "I'll have to be off to Raven Hall."

"Tek mi dogs wi' yuh," warned the old platelayer Blaster. "A night like this yuh is likely to see anything about."

"Anything?" queried Joe.

"The Gamekeeper's ghost do you mean?" asked a W.A.A.F.

"I was thinking more of Dracula."

"What's yuh dogs for?" asked Frank.

"The not me own dogs. They're me Master's dogs. He left them wi' me when he went off. The ole master never went out on a night like this without his dogs. He always said he expected Dracula back one clear night."

"We're expected to ask, 'Why back?' Aren't we Blaster?" asked the amused but sceptical sergeant as he rose to go.

"Why back?" echoed Joe.

"He landed here one night looking for blood and souls. Thought it were Whitby. He were seen on t' battlements."

"We'd better go as well, Betty," spoke one of the W.A.A.F.s to her companion. "We're on duty. Anyway we've heard it before."

"Yes, you have," agreed the old ganger seriously, "But not on a night like this. An' when war's ranging through his homeland in Transylvania."

"You're frightening me?" laughed the sergeant. "Come on let's go. Let these lads get to bed or whatever they do on a night like this."

"Don't turn in yet." said a W.A.A.F. to Joe and Frank. "Come to our post just for a few minutes. A night cap, Sarge."

It seemed to be good idea so Frank and Joe agreed without any discussion. Blaster joined them with the two dogs on the joint leash. "I'll come wi' yuh and see if the dogs say anything's queer tonight."

They trudged through the deep snow across station square and the footings of the old unfinished 'New Town' development that had left a half-exposed network of street foundations and drains. Despite the thick snow and ice and the unlit night they could see the shape of the development. The North Sea caught the moonlight and from the height of Ravenscar presented a calm but undulating surface. The absence of the biting, fierce wind made the short evening walk through the snow to Raven Hall pleasant in the company of the W.A.A.F.s, the sergeant and the talkative Blaster.

"Can't you help these lads? They ought to be sleeping somewhere better than that wooden waiting-room," asked one of the W.A.A.F.s.

"We ought to be at home in Castlebrough. Would be if Big Ted hadn't cast us adrift," grumbled Frank.

"Okay," replied the the army sergeant, "I'll have a word with the O.I.C. You know about security in our place though."

"Let me tek 'em 'round the garden tosh," suggested Blaster. "Just like to show 'em the battlements and terraces where Dracula's said to have landed."

"Five minutes that's all, after that I'm gone," said the sergeant.

"We'll go too. Just five minutes. We'll see you in the hallway," stated one of the W.A.A.F.s.

"No more than ten minutes. If you do I'm gone," answered the sergeant. "And you Blaster don't go down the terraces there's still mines and wire down there."

The battlements on the seaward side stood as gaunt silhouettes, sharp and geometric against the star-studded sky towards the east. Stone statues of dogs and ravens in the gardens attracted Blaster's dogs as they growled and prowled, still restrained by the joint lead they shared. Gulls and jackdaws wheeled in the sky above the battlements and screeched. Blaster pointed to bats that swooped in black silhouette and made their contribution to the noises of the night. The trees in the garden murmured as Blaster listened carefully and not a light betrayed the presence of Raven Hall Hotel.

"It were just here as one Emily Tragg an' her sister saw the vampire Dracula, 'bout fifty years ago, just when't railway were new."

"What exactly did they say they saw?" Joe couldn't restrain a show of interest in spite of his scepticism.

"Come on you two. Up the steps." He pulled on the dogs' lead and tried to encourage them up the steps onto the battlement walk-ways. "Want to get up here so's we can all look over down the cliff." He pulled harder. "Yuh won't have it will yuh, yuh pesky brutes." Joe recorded a feeling that they were doing just what Blaster wanted them to do. "They ain't goin' to have it, They think summat's there," stated Blaster.

"What did Emily say she saw?" asked Joe again.

"She sez, her an' 'er sister sez, there was a huge bird, as big as a man on the battlements," replied Blaster. "More like a cloaked figure of a man. Some says it were a vampire. And does tha know it were the same night as Mr Hammond's sister were passing away in the east wing guest bedroom."

"Suppose she had bite wounds on 'er throat," chipped in the scornful Joe.

"You've heard this before, haven't yuh son?"

"Was there an inquest?" asked Frank.

"There was. She died from loss o' blood from a throat wound. Mr Hammond put it about that she cut 'er own throat. He would. Didna want it abroad that a vampire, a human vampire had done it, and sucked her blood. Wouldn't get guests staying in the 'otel, if that got around. But it 'as got around because of Emily an' her sister saying they'd seen an apparition. An' they'd never heard of Dracula having been here in the past."

"What yer pulling on the dogs for Blaster? They don't want to go up the steps do they?" asked a W.A.A.F.

"No they don't. I could mek 'em. But they'd whimper and growl. An' we don't have time. The sergeant's fittin' yuh up wi' somewhere to sleep. Yuh'd better get back to the Hall before he goes."

The oak panelled, stone-flagged entrance hall in Raven Hall Hotel was commodious and pleasant even though it did show the wear and tear of the forces' wartime occupation. The girls booked in with the duty officer and disappeared with gentle waves and smiles. Frank and Joe waited where the sergeant had directed. "Have you got all your gear lads?" he asked when he emerged from an open door into the hall.

"We've only got our bait-tins and books and papers over in the waiting-room," answered Joe.

"Go and get them. Don't tell anyone you're coming over here. We've got security to think about. Don't want to cause a precedent for Homeless Hectors. Be off now. I've only got half an hour."

The trudge back to the waiting-room took only a few minutes but there was time for Frank to giggle and speculate. "Wonder if we're going to sleep with them two birds. The fat one was ogling you, Joe."

"I suppose the good lookin' one was ogling you," retorted Joe. They collected their bits and piled the bags and carpets on the straw palliasse. Joe then tore a page from his note-book and wrote, 'Thanks. We've moved to other digs'. They placed the note on the pile of carpets and coverings, turned down the lamps and returned full of anticipation across station square to Raven Hall Hotel.

"You ready lads? Keep your coats on we're going out again," the sergeant instructed as he collected them from the hall. They passed through rooms and passages and emerged in the garden at the back of the main building. "These are the lads, Captain. I haven't briefed them," he said to the officer whom they approached.

"Okay, sergeant. I'll brief them." He turned to the shadowy figure a little to his rear. "This is Corporal Thompson of the the East Yorks Yeomanry," he informed Frank and Joe. "Now watch where you step. I've got a light. Keep on my heels and take care. You," he tugged on Frank's sleeve, "follow closely behind the corporal." He started a gentle descent down the slope of the path. It gets a bit rough in places, a bit narrower too. Icy as well. Sometimes there's a rope. Sometimes a handrail. Just go slow."

They left the garden through a postern gate in the battlements, then made an easy descent down terraces, steps and a carefully laid pathway to the undercliff leading to broken ground littered with large boulders, bracken and low shrubs.

"Blaster were told that there was mines and wire on the terraces," Joe informed nervously.

"Yes. But do as we tell you and you'll come to no harm."

"Where to, Sir? Where we going?" asked Joe, with some surprise, as they all moved off.

"You're going to Castlebrough, Where else?"

"Good!" exclaimed Joe with obvious relief. "That's good, isn't it Frank?" Frank's reply was missed in the shuffling of feet and the brushing of undergrowth and bracken as the footway became more overgrown and uneven.

"See that up there," the officer added, pointing to the star studded clear sky. "The constellation of Orion. There's the Plough. Could you point out the North Star?" asked the officer of Joe. "Young fellow in transport should know his way around the Heavens. Do you navigate by compass and the stars on them things you drive?" He laughed and chatted on. "You panting and you're a lot younger than me. You should see what it's like coming up this way. It's a ruddy climb. Especially with a pack on."

Joe gave up the task of trying to respond. He concentrated on the descent which took quite some time. Sometimes they walked for a short while on almost level ground, then they would descend steeply, guided by ropes or simple wooden handrails, or forced to divert to avoid barbed wire. They could clearly see out into the bay and even pick out the shadowy patch that was the large fishing village of Robin Hood's Bay on the coast in the distance, though not a single light revealed it presence. 'How far to the road?' Joe asked himself as they slowly dropped down to lower levels.

"This bit's steeper, but it's quite safe. Get your hands on the rope and go carefully." The scrub and heather had given way to taller undergrowth, bushes and small trees, They wound down hill now, blanketed in darkness and shrouded by small trees and then, treated to a glint of sky and stars. The sea was noisier now, the tide was rolling in and breaking on rocks and gravel, the sounds of the rollers were unmistakable. The single file of walkers emerged from the small trees and undergrowth onto a muddy boulder-strewn shore. They were clear of snow and ice, the sea washed and rolled not far away and they were below the high tide mark. The stars and the moon picked out the horizon clearly.

"Where's the road?"asked Joe.

"There isn't one. What do you want a road for?"

"Thought there must be one down to Robin Hood's Bay," said Joe.

"Thought you wanted to go to Castlebrough?" queried the captain.

"We do. But how are we going to get there. I thought we were going on an army lorry," volunteered Joe.

"You know what thought did. Well, remember it, an' stop thinking."

"Well how are you going to get us to Castlebrough?" asked Frank with emphasis.

"Look out over there, coming in quietly, only a shadow. You'll hear him if you listen." They focussed their ears and their eyes, Yes, they could hear the gentle throbbing of an engine on very low power. "He's coming in carefully to that little wooden departure point."

"What's happening, captain?" queried Joe.

"You aren't supposed to know. Mum's the word, it's still the word. So don't go spreading it about how you got home."

"How are we getting home?" asked Joe, only because he was closest to the captain. If he hadn't asked, Frank would have asked.

"On the boat. You'll be on the fish pier at Castlebrough in thirty minutes."

"Bloody hell," Frank responded with loud alarm. "I don't like sailing on the bloody Mere, never mind the bloody sea at night."

The Captain was indicating the motor launch with his hand-held light. It came quietly inshore to the temporary landing platform. Unused to such night-time activity, Joe and Frank blundered when they boarded the launch and had to endure wet feet and trousers.

"Who we with, Captain?" asked Frank nervously as he looked over the side of the boat at the lapping sea.

"Do you need to know? You know I said it's, 'Mum's the word'," said the Captain.

"He does," said Joe bravely. "His Mam might ask him."

"Coast Guard. When we drop you off at the fish pier, I'll hand you in to the coast guard. They're expecting you."

The sea, though choppy, was not unfriendly, it merely rolled them about, and raised them up, then dipped them into troughs. Soon Frank and Joe wondered where their inner organs were. The crew of three and the passengers avoided conversation; the crew scanned the seascape and the coast. Only the faintest fore and aft lights betrayed their presence visually. The headlands of the coastline passed by on their starboard side and provided some shadow for cover. They motored southwards until the tall headland surmounted by the silhouette of ancient Castlebrough castle appeared. The sea rolled more viciously as it battled with the turbulent currents of the bay and the large jutting headland. Joe retched over the side of the boat and rabbit stew, Nesfield's Mild and John Lamb's rum went to feed the fishes. Frank couldn't ignore the example and he joined the suffering. They couldn't suppress the groans and moans; Joe was sure he was going to die, and 'On the day he'd just qualified for his first year fireman's pay.' How cruel, and 'On the day he'd blown his firebox fusible plugs.' How lucky that he was going to die and not face the music. Frank rolled into the bottom of the boat and retched again. Both suffered for an eternity, until they tried to respond to the voice that proclaimed, "We're here." The motor launch bumped against the quay-side and they howled at the final indignity as the voice continued, "Come on. All off. And that includes you two old Castlebrough Sea Salts." The voice chortled on, "Help 'em up the steps, you Jake and Mike."

Frank and Joe flopped on a seat-high stack of fish boxes, and froze in the bitter sea breeze, and died again and again until the retching subsided. "Come in here for a few moments, lads. We're just having kippers for supper." A jolly voice invited them into the coast guard office, a voice that laughed when it mentioned the kippers.

They entered as instructed. There were no kippers. Instead they were granted quiet recovery time, a time that was finally punctuated by Frank's weak question, "What time is it?"

"Five-past-seven," was the reply.

Joe came to life with a sickly response, "Bloody hell, I thought weeks had gone by."

"Hey you railway lads. Do yuh want a lift to the station? There's a Sutton's lorry taking the fish up for the eight o' clock York train."

They couldn't say 'no'. They'd better go. They might still need the hospital. The throbbing front seats in the cab of the fish lorry, and the stink, and the slow pulsating haul by the lorry up the blacked-out, steep Castlebrough High Street seemed to confirm their sure death scenario. They were still retching when the lorry drew alongside the concrete fish stage outside Castlebrough station parcels' office.

"What a bloody way to earn a crust, isn't it Joe?" growled Frank as they both hauled themselves onto the footplate of Arthur Wilko's D49 loco that was just about to leave number two platform for Castlebrough loco shed. "Lord, never again will I go to sea."

"We ain't got to tell anybody about that," responded Joe forcefully. "It was unofficial. Might get the sack for skating off from Ravenscar, never mind going to sea on the L.N.E.R's payroll. Good Lord. I'm in enough trouble already."

"It's good to see Washbeck Cabin, an' the loco yard. Quite busy too. Snow's under control here." Frank rambled on as the engine progressed towards the loco shed, a sure sign that he was recovering.

They were signalled past the loco yard push-bell cabin entrance to the yard because the 8 p.m. York train engine was leaving for the station. Arthur Wilko's D49 locomotive was directed to enter at the south end of the yard by Gas Works cabin.

"Just over an hour an' half since, we were drinking with them two W.A.A.F.s in the church hall at Ravenscar," commented Joe. "Amazing isn't it?" He paused and looked harder across the loco yard. A few hand lamps carried by moving working figures and the subdued light from the yard gas lamp standards illuminated the frozen snow-covered yard. Snowplough box cars and an engine were being moved into the first road of the loco coal sidings. "Look Frank, snowploughs, with a G5 loco. But that isn't Big Ted in the cab, that's Jingo driving, and Johnny Marsay walking."

"You're right Joe. They look like the snowploughs we had. How have they got here? Big Ted might be still around."

Arthur Wilko's loco entered the yard and the two lads went off towards the ploughs. They learned that Big Ted and his Malton mate had just left the yard aboard the locomotive that was working the 8 p.m. express to York. They were going home to Malton on the cushions. They had just brought the ploughs in from Pickering. The ploughs were needed to open the road to Ravenscar and Whitby on the morrow. Every other railway was cleared. Frank and Joe volunteered no information, just received what Johnny Marsay said and walked to the eight-laned shed and to the store office.

Joe felt sick with apprehension as well as from the sea journey. "He's been and spiked my guns. The lousy beggar. He's come back here just to shop me."

"I wouldn't worry Joe. Just think you've got your first year's firing in. You're on first year fireman's pay every day from now on until you get your second year in."

"It's alright for you, Frank you aren't on the carpet. I hope Franker

isn't here tonight. He might just be with all this snow we've had."
Another eternity reigned for Joe as he plodded down the shed, his feet
and legs still wet-through from splashing in the sea when boarding the
launch. His heart was as heavy as a brick-arch fire-brick, and he still
had to face his Mother who would have expected him home at mid-
day. And he'd missed a planned visit to friend Dan, he'd been going
to go with him to the Odeon cinema tonight to see 'Casablanca' and
Humphrey Bogart.

Bill Clarke was the only occupant of the loco store and time-office.
He wasn't in a talkative mood and made Joe wait while he completed
a writing task at the store desk. Neither Joe nor Frank broke the ice.
Eventually, he said, "Make you're own sheets out today, seeing
you've both been with Malton men. Did they make it onto the 8 o'
clock York train?" Frank and Joe replied where they couldn't afford
not to reply. "Show on the sheet that your engine failed at Ravenscar
and that you've left it there. Dead as a bloody gate-post I hear."

"Yes," Joe replied timidly.

"That's one for the books, I must say. Dropping your fusible plugs.
Can't say I've ever heard of that before. You're going to be famous.
You'll have your name on a stone tablet at headquarters. Hope there
are some extenuating circumstances."

"There was the snow, high as that door in places."

"That's no excuse. That's snow excuse." He laughed at his own
humour.

Joe was in a dream as he departed from Frank Sutton and made his
way slowly up Hastings Road. "I'll have to look that word up,
'extenuating', 'extenuating circumstances', I might just need it," Joe
muttered audibly.

1
Showing Initiative.

The Castlebrough branch of the National Union of Railwaymen opened its fortnightly Sunday morning meeting in the British Legion Social Club. "Are you ready Bill?" the branch chairman asked the secretary.

"Yes, but Joe Wade isn't here yet to take the minutes. He said he was definitely coming because he had an issue to raise. In the meantime we'll go through the minutes of the last meeting," answered the secretary.

"We'll start then," said the chairman. "Can we have the minutes of the last meeting, please Bill?" While Bill obliged with a reading of the minutes, Joe slipped into the room and took his seat alongside the secretary. Joe was Minutes Secretary and soon settled to the task. Locomotive men were a very tiny minority of those attending. Nearly all locomotive men were members of the Associated Society of Locomotive Engineers and Firemen but Joe had become a member of the National Union of Railwaymen when he was 'War Acting Lad Parcels Porter Joseph Wade' from the age of fifteen and he had continued his membership after his appointment to the Motive Power Department.

"They'll never look after a locoman if there's a conflict of interest between a footplate man and another railwayman," went a regular statement and belief of A.S.L.E.F. members. At the moment Joe was wondering if this was so, he was faced with serious disciplinary action over the loss of his engine at Ravenscar and he was an N.U.R. man and Big Ted Coney was an A.S.L.E.F. man. Would the N.U.R. fight as hard for Joe as A.S.L.E.F. would for Ted? Would they really understand the nature of the locoman's job?

The discussion was on politics. It was on a resolution demanding the full implementation of the Beveridge Report. "Nothing to do with this meeting," said the last speaker. "It's politics. Leave it to the political parties. I say it's out of order Mister Chairman."

"You're overruled Jack," said the chairman, "it's the proper business of the meeting." So was the discussion on affiliation to the Labour Party, the discussion on the new Representation of the People's Act, the strike action against Sunday work that was disrupting Liverpool and other places, the free postal courses on Economics, English and Arithmetic, and the One Week Residential Summer School at Ruskin College at Oxford.....

The mood and discussion amongst the railway staff and in the unions had politicised, motivated and educated Joe in a way that school had not. He was beginning to learn to work out percentages, be introduced to fractions which he could not recollect doing at school and he was learning about adjectives and adverbs. The conflicting views of the Independent Labour Party, the Communist Party and the Labour Party, and their joint dismissal of the Liberals and the Conservative Party were food for his hungry mind. Bert was called a Trotskyist. The absent Fred was described as having been a Mosleyite who'd seen the error of his ways. Another talked of the Stalinists, only to be punctuated by "You can't do without a King and Queen." Joe had found a cauldron of ideas which boiled in him a desire to learn and change things in his own small way.

"Any other business?" asked the chairman as the meeting drew to a close.

"Yes, me, I have," Joe called to the chairman. "Can the meeting help me with a problem I have?"

"That's what we're here for," answered the chairman.

"I've had a misfortune, an accident maybe. I don't know how to describe it."

"Try then. That's what we're here for."

"Well, you see," Joe muttered uncertainly. He didn't know how to proceed. He didn't want to say that he'd run out of steam and water and ruined his engine. Any description of the misdeed seemed to condemn him. "Well I've got notification of a disciplinary matter against me. I really don't know what to do."

"Well for a start," came in Jack, who was always telling the chairman about the proper order and interpretation of business, "It's confidential if it's a disciplinary matter, and especially if it involves another member."

"Yes, Jack, we know that, but we've got to know what he wants help with?"

"Well, don't let him tell any names of other members who might be involved."

"That's fair enough Jack," ruled the chairman.

Joe began, with a feeling of uncertainty caused by Jack's 'official' way of going about things. "Well I've got this official letter asking, nay, telling me, to see the shed master, and a loco inspector to show reason why disciplinary action should not be taken against me."

"Does it just involve you son?" came a voice from the body of the meeting.

"It involves others. But it may be a sacking job, so I've been told."

"Best thing, son," joined in Bill Branson, the knowledgeable and authoritative Branch Secretary, "is ask our member Jim Simpson to be your spokesman and representative. You know who he is. Just write in the minute book that 'the branch approved that a request for personal representation be referred to Jim Simpson, Branch Vice-Chairman.'"

Joe muttered his thanks as the meeting broke up. He felt a bit deflated by the knock-about that his simple request caused, but he was beginning to learn about the rough and ready working class democracy that solved many problems. He could now consult Jim Simpson about his disciplinary problem.

He left by himself knowing only that dinner at home with all the family was to take place. That in itself was an unusual occurrence because both his brother Tim and his father were to be at home together on the first occasion for a long time and also Joe was not required to work. He walked out of the club down the ice-covered steps almost into a waiting young woman who clearly was a few years older than he.

"Has John Burton left yet?" she asked Joe.

"There wasn't a John Burton in our union meeting."

"I must have got something wrong. I was told he would be at the A.S.L.E.F. meeting here."

"I made a record of all those who attended the meeting I've just been at," said Joe, "and he wasn't there. Actually it was an N.U.R. meeting."

"Oh, so you're a railwayman. You might know my Father, John Burton, he's a railwayman. Works at the shed."

"I do. You don't mean Jack Burton? 'Fifty Bob' Burton. We call him 'Fifty Bob' Burton because he's always dressed so smartly in a suit. Looks like a model in the shop window of the Fifty Bob Tailors."

"Yes, we at home always call him John."

"He's an A.S.L.E.F. man. I've just been to the N.U.R. meeting."

"I'll go and see if I can catch him at home down Sander Road."

"Do you mind if I walk with you," asked Joe? "I'm walking down that way to deliver this book I borrowed off someone. It's safer to walk than to ride a bike through this rutted ice."

"Yes it is," she returned. "Is it a good book, a novel?"

"I'm not into reading novels. This is 'The Proper Study of Mankind' by Howard."

"That sounds deep. What is the proper study then?"

"Mankind" replied Joe proudly. "The proper study of mankind is man in the world and the environment. The proper study is not God but man."

"Are you an atheist then?"

"I don't know what I am. I want to study the world and man and find out where they are going."

"You sound so brainy. Do you go to classes? Worker's Educational Association classes?"

Joe didn't, but he did study trade union postal courses and read books that were passed around the men at the shed. His current rage was Darwin's 'The Origin of Species' and the 'Descent of Man'. During his walk he learnt that Julie Burton was a school teacher and that she went to Bill Evans' weekly Hull University Extension classes on 'World Affairs' at Roscoe Rooms and another class in Modern Russian Literature. Joe was impressed. He walked taller in the presence of this teacher. Yes, he would like to join the 'World Affairs class'. Yes, he would go with her next Tuesday. He was becoming more interested in her. He now noticed she had a nice oval face and blue eyes. He didn't think about his destroyed engine until he left her, and then it returned to nag him.

★ ★ ★ ★

"Will you change jobs with me tomorrow Johnny?" Joe asked, "I'm down for afternoon station pilot and you're on afternoon Gallows Close pilot with Jim Simpson." John Marsay had complied readily because working on the passenger station pilot was more interesting than shunting goods wagons about for eight hours. Joe sought the change because Jim Simpson and the Gallows pilot engine had been instructed to make time during the day's work and travel to Ravenscar and recover the dead and damaged J21. Joe had greater interest in the recovery than anyone else. A week had elapsed since that eventful day when the twins had been born and Joe's job had been put on the line.

Jim had already been acquainted with the facts as Joe saw them and he persuaded the shed master and the locomotive inspector to delay the disciplinary procedure until the loco was recovered and examined.

"We'll do a couple of hours shunting to get the urgent work done then we'll go to Ravenscar," Ken, the shunter on duty, proclaimed to Jim and Joe on the A6 tank engine in Gallows Close yard. "We'll go over to Belford's sidings soon, as well, there's some old bags of cement being thrown out, they are good enough for me to repair our kitchen floor."

Joe's ears pricked up. If there was old cement being dumped he also had a use for some. When they visited Belford's siding and the builder's yard, to enable Ken place his two bags on the outside footplate, Joe placed two for himself. When Ken's had been taken to a safe dry place to reside until he could take them home on his bicycle Joe's two were left on the front-end near the smokebox.

"We'll make our trip to Ravenscar after the next train from Castlebrough clears the section to Cloughton," said Ken.

Joe enlightened them about the destination of his two bags of cement as they departed along the Whitby line. "I've got an allotment just the other side of Coldyhill Lane bridge. Will you stop Jim, while I drop these two bags over the fence?"

"What the heck are you doing with cement?" asked Jim"

"Building a pigsty with Dan West for us to keep pigs in."

"But ain't he Tom West's lad and in a wheelchair?"

Ken broke in and inadvertently helped Joe at a sensitive moment when Joe's driver might have blown-up about being asked to stop on the line near Scalby. "I never thought about using the engine to take the cement where I wanted it. When we come back we'll pick mine up and take it to the shed down Sander Road, I live just opposite the shed so I can carry it home, save pushing it on me bike."

"Will you help me off with my two, Ken?" asked Joe.

Jim Simpson found he'd been organised without giving his consent. "It'd be nice to be asked," he stated in a light tone.

"Sorry Jim, I was going to but I couldn't catch your ear. We were so busy."

Jim brought the loco to a halt by the road bridge. "Mek it sharp you two, don't want to be blocking this section."

"We'll only be half-a-minute, Jim," chipped in Ken helpfully. "Just chuck 'em over the fence. Won't we son?"

"Sort of," replied Joe. He didn't tell Ken that he'd have to scramble over the fence and unlock his little garden shed before they could put the cement over the fence. The snow posed problems. Although the lines and sidings were fairly clear of snow, quite deep drifts still occupied the linesides. Joe and Ken had quite an embarrassing job struggling through the deep snow and over the fence with two one-hundred-weight bags of cement.

Their arrival at Ravenscar was painful for Joe. His dead, ice-covered J21 in the siding where they had left it was a grave sight to him, he became quieter, his harmless cockiness disappeared. They entered the siding and coupled their A6 to the J21 and tested the through-brake. Ken would have to ride as guard on the dirty cold J21 and he expressed his displeasure as they waited while the line to Castlebrough became available. Joe spent the time looking around

Ravenscar, the hotel and station square, with Jim's assertion ringing in his ears 'Not to float off and get lost.' Joe felt as though he were visiting the site of a dream, he felt relieved when they were underway, down the one-in-forty incline to Stainton Dale, Cloughton and eventually Castlebrough.

"Put it at the bottom of number two road, just outside the fitter's shop," instructed Arthur the shed fitter in charge. They ran around the J21 and propelled it into number two road in the main locomotive shed. "I see there have been a few repair cards in for this engine. It's been reported for priming and it hasn't had a boiler wash-out since it was reported," the fitter told Simpson who detailed the nature of examination to which he would like the shed fitter subject the locomotive. "There's a limit to what I can find out about the engine when it's not in steam," concluded the fitter.

The loco became a subject of interest to other loco and shed staff. 'Never seen a loco that's dropped it's plugs.' 'What a bloody mess. You'll get an Irishman's rise for this Joe.' 'Running wi'out steam and watter, eh Joe? Now you've managed it you'll have to patent how to do it.' The stream of jocular remarks inundated Joe.

'Was it something to be proud of?' Joe asked himself. He felt almost famous as the centre of attention but he reacted in the same light-hearted manner. He was relieved to see Ken back from the delivery of his two bags of cement and receive instructions to return to Gallows Close.

★ ★ ★ ★

"I'd really like to go to sea." Dan West was commenting on Joe's account of the boat trip from Ravenscar to the fish pier at Castlebrough. They were playing draughts at Dan's bedside, a game which had become a real passion for both of them.

"Don't tell your dad about me coming back by sea," emphasised Joe. "We told everyone that we were brought down in an army lorry on side roads. Yuh Dad's L.D.C. Secretary at the shed an' I don't want him to know." That was only part of Joe's reason for not wanting Tom West to know, the other part was Tom's loud mouth, he couldn't have kept the knowledge to himself. Joe didn't want his version of the truth contradicted by anyone, but especially by Tom.

"I was at the Graham Sea Training School and I intended to go in the Royal Navy," explained Dan. "Reckon I've had it now unless there's some way of making me better and walking again."

"That's what we're after with this letter from Queen Elizabeth. You know that you're going somewhere. They've said that."

"George next door, yuh know him, locoman before he joined up, says he could take me out to sea on the boat that belongs to his mate. He's on leave now. Would you go with us?"

"Lord! Not after the last lot. I were sick for a week."

"Yuh get used to that if yuh keeps going."

"I don't want to get used to it thank you. I always wanted to join the navy as you did, but now I'm cured."

"Yeller, that's what you are. I'll go by myself with George."

"Can you?"

"If you give me a lift into the boat wi' George."

"Set it up then. I'll come down and help George to lift you from the quayside into the boat. An' if you come back I'll help lift you out. If you don't I'll throw a wreath on the sea from the far pier."

"Bloody good mate you are!" laughed Dan from his bed in the front room. "I'll set it up."

★ ★ ★ ★

"It's choppy an' cold George," quivered Dan in his wheelchair alongside the harbour.

"Bracing, that's what I call it," responded George. "Ideal for a night's fishing."

"What do yuh mean, a night's fishing?" returned Dan. "We're just dangling these handlines over the side for five minutes aren't we Joe?"

"We aren't dangling anything. You are. I told you not to buy a line for me," retorted Joe.

On the pier close to the boat Dan asked, "Where's the tide?"

"Down there," explained George who was pushing the chair. He indicated with a pointing finger that the tide level was well down the harbour wall.

"How yuh getting the boat up here?" asked Dan.

"We're taking you down the steps to it."

"Are we? I'm not going," stated Joe.

"Give me a lift down, yeller begger," scorned Dan. "Never win the war with the likes of him in the navy would we?" The hair-raising descent down the seaweed covered steps stayed Dan and Joe from further comments.

A fisherman's voice carried from the pier edge said, "You must be bloody crazy going out in that old boat. It ain't seaworthy. It's top heavy." Grunts of agreement came from mates who accompanied him.

"What do they know about it?" asked George.

"They're only fishermen, been fishermen all their lives," answered Joe.

"Not proper seamen," comforted George.

"Goodbye," shouted the fishermen who waved from above as the cabin-topped motor boat chugged away towards the harbour mouth and the heaving expanse beyond with Joe unwillingly aboard.

George was at the tiller behind the makeshift cabin. The petrol engine was positioned and uncovered in the bottom of the boat towards the front end where the subdued Joe and Dan were sat in the bows on the wooden seat.

"Thought you weren't coming Joe?"

"I thought I wasn't," answered Joe.

"Don't go too far out George, it's getting choppy."

"An it's a long way from Castlebrough. Look how far it is," said Joe weakly.

"Don't go too far George," pleaded Dan.

"Thought you wanted to fish."

"Yes, but not on the Dogger Bank."

"He thinks he's on the bloody Queen Mary. Just cos he's got his uniform on," replied Joe, who was feeling more and more concerned as the distance increased and the sea became more lively, more turbulent.

"We'll stop in five minutes. We want the good fish don't we?"

"No!" replied Joe honestly.

"Bait up your lines. Let's see if we can catch our supper."

Obediently they fished and secretly hoped they wouldn't catch anything and complicate even further their wretched lives. The heaving sea was beginning to swill the contents of their stomachs around. Dan expressed the fear that he might get a bite on his line and be pulled overboard. Joe, who couldn't swim, wondered how he'd save Dan if the boat was swamped by the sea. He had heard it said that paraplegics floated in water because of their paralysed limbs, maybe Dan would make a good lifebelt for both of them.

"Very cold now George," volunteered Joe, then sheepishly asked, "When are we going back?"

"You're not wanting to go back home already are you?" asked George.

Joe hesitated. Dan said, "He does."

"Shall we make for home then?" inquired George.

The response, "Please," from Joe and "Yes" from Dan was enough to persuade the Royal Navy sailor in charge. The engine stuttered into life and they started their thankful journey towards the distant

Castlebrough and the swilling feeling multiplied. The engine crackled as its heat accumulated and the exhaust pipe smoked.

"Burning oil," shouted Dan to George who leaned forward from the tiller and looked at the engine.

"It's that rubber flexible pipe on the cold feed to the water jacket. It's burning 'cos it's touching up to the hot exhaust. You'll have to bend it clear Joe?" He didn't tell him to take care, he knew that he would.

Joe protected his hand with his handkerchief and grasped the small gauge copper pipe that came upwards through the bottom of the boat. He pressed gently to change its direction and divert the flexible rubber extending connection away from the adjacent smouldering exhaust. He was surprised to feel cold seawater on his fingers, even more surprised as he moved to find that the pipe had broken away in his hand. "Look" he said, casting his eyes in the skipper's direction. He needn't have issued the instruction because both Dan and George were observing the vital task being performed. They could clearly see the broken copper pipe sticking through the bottom of the boat and spouting a jet of seawater upwards and then downwards into the bilges of the boat.

"I knew that I shouldn't have come," said Joe.

"I knew you shouldn't," reprimanded Dan.

"What now George? I can't just let it fill the boat."

"Put your bloody finger on it, daft sod," offered Dan, more in condemnation than in advice.

"That's no good!" called George, "We want that water to go around the engine to cool it. Hold the two pipe ends together and hope enough water gets round the engine to keep it going."

The journey took an age. The engine became hotter, the shoreline ever tantalisingly closer. The two landlubbers' stomachs swilled more violently as they rode the tide and the mounting surf. Joe uttered his second prayer to the North Sea and the comforting embrace of the two piers offered to draw them into the safety of the harbour.

"Yuh're back then," called out the fisherman on the pier who had warned them during their embarkation.

"Course we are. Did you think we'd gone to Germany?" replied George.

"What's the fire in the middle of the boat?"

"Have you sold your catch to Suttons? When will it be auctioned?"

"Should ban boats like that."

The remarks from the seafarers came thick and fast as George and Joe struggled up the steps to the pier with Dan stretched between them like a rag doll, except that his hands and arms strove to grasp any rail or offered hand in desperation.

"Did yuh enjoy that son?" a grinning trawlerman asked Dan as they settled him in the waiting wheelchair.

"Yes," retched Dan. "We're going again when you aren't here to warn the fish that we're coming."

★ ★ ★ ★

2
JUDGEMENT DAY.

Nine-thirty in the morning was the appointed time for Joe's trial and execution. At least that was his private description of the event. He didn't put any knowledge around the shed, why should he? Railwaymen often faced discipline for violations of some expected behaviour, and they didn't bother making an issue out of their defence like he was bent on doing. Mostly, a 'Form One Warning' or a 'Caution' would be accepted as part of the job and of the loco shed master's duty to insist on high standards. But when a sacking or a suspension might be a possible result it was better to prepare a good defence. Joe was ready, or more correctly Jim Simpson was ready.

"This is Locomotive Inspector Brown," said Mr Franker as the two locomen seated themselves in Franker's inner office, "That's Jim Simpson, N.U.R. representative and this young chap as you might expect is Joe Wade." Nods were exchanged and cups of tea provided by the clerk were handed around. "We know why we are here so we might as well let you make a start. Inspector Brown and I will listen to your case and make a joint report and recommendation. Are you going to kick off Joe? You know the basic facts are that you let your water level fall to such a low level on J21 number 1516 that the fusible plugs melted and disabled the loco when in traffic."

"Yes, those are the facts," replied Joe with a determination that they weren't going to make him take the blame. He stopped and waited.

"What then?" encouraged the shed master.

"Simply, I was told by Driver Coney not to put the injector on because we didn't have enough steam."

"But why didn't you put it on? You were the fireman, and the boiler was your responsibility." Locomotive Inspector Brown was being provocative.

"Cos I was told not to."

"Do you always do what your driver tells you? Especially when you're with a strange driver on a road you're familiar with as a fireman."

"Well I do. I think I do. Well not always. Just depends what it is he wants me to do?"

"In this case he told you not to put water in the boiler, and you did just what he said even though, I believe, you knew that the water level was dangerously low."

"Yes."

"Were there any extenuating circumstances?"

"Oh." Joe paused, he knew he should have looked that word up after the man at the meeting used it. He bent forward and whispered in Jim Simpson's ear that he did not understand the question. Jim replied quietly to Joe who then said, "Mr Simpson is going to deal with the extenuating circumstances."

"Let's hear them now," said the inspector turning to Jim Simpson.

Jim started. "The problems on the road are very important but I want to draw your attention to events before the ploughs took off on their journey from here to Pickering and then over the Goathland Summit to Whitby and, eventually to Ravenscar. What time did you sign on duty Joe?"

"Four a.m. on the station pilot."

"What time did you finish your shift the day before?"

"Seven-fifteen p.m."

"Were you aware that you got only eight hours and forty-five minutes rest between shifts, that is between signing off for rest and signing on for duty on the station pilot?"

"Yes I was."

"But you should have had nine-hours off duty rest under the regulations that cover safety. You know that." Jim continued as Joe nodded. "Why did you agree to sign on under the stipulated rest period?"

"There were a lot of reasons. No one else could do the job that early. And I was told to come fifteen minutes late in order to get my nine hours rest off the job, but, last of all, I was keen because that firing shift qualified for my first-year fireman's pay."

"You'd done seventeen hours when you clocked off on the day you dropped the plugs, hadn't you?"

Joe nodded. He wasn't now so sure that Jim Simpson was helping him.

"You joined the snowploughs that had come in from Malton with driver Coney of Malton and his passed fireman Jack Post. You became Ted Coney's fireman on engine 1516 the J21. Frank Sutton became Jack Post's fireman on the G5 Malton engine, then the four of you took the two snow ploughs to Pickering and then on to Whitby and finally to Ravenscar." Joe kept nodding agreement as Jim Simpson dragged it all out. "What was the condition of the J21 when you and Jack Coney took it out of the shed?"

"Well it was dead at first. It had some steam pressure in the boiler but no fire. It had been stopped for repairs. But an engine was needed to get the two ploughs round those roads where there was heavy snow so we lit it up quickly with fire from the furnace."

"Did you get coal?"

"No they were out of coal on the coal stage. Snow had blocked the bank to the stage and they couldn't get wagons up the bank. So we made do with the rubbish on board. We didn't have much time to get out and sweep the roads through Pickering and Whitby."

"How did the engine steam when you were on the road?"

"Not very well. It was in a bit of a state," replied Joe. "Every steam joint seemed to blow. There wasn't much blast on the fire, but we managed alright. I've had plenty of experience," Joe concluded proudly. "I've got my first year in."

"You're seventeen now aren't you?"

"Eighteen in four months."

"I'll just break off from you for a minute Joe." Jim Simpson looked at Franker and Brown, "Let me tell you about the report the fitter put in after examining the engine when Joe and I brought it back from Ravenscar eight days after it dropped it plugs in the tunnel."

"It didn't drop its plugs in the tunnel, just after it," corrected Joe.

"Yes I know." replied Jim Simpson, rather irritated by Joe's interjection. "There are four relevant points I want to make about the state of the engine.

"First," he emphasised his enumeration. "It had been stopped the previous day for urgent repairs which didn't get done because of traffic needs. If it hadn't been because of the war and the snow emergency it would not have been in traffic that day."

"Second," he paused again for effect. "The engine had been priming badly and was stopped for a boiler wash-out, which it didn't get. If it had been washed out my bet is that the boiler-smith would have changed the plugs if only because they hadn't been changed for three months."

"Third, the engine had, still has, a serious blow on the saturated side of the superheater header. Not only did it cause a waste of steam but it weakened the smokebox vacuum and reduced the blast on the fire."

"Fourthly, the tube plate was badly scarred with clinker and some tubes were blocked. In short the engine wasn't fit to be on the road with an experienced fireman never mind a seventeen year old cleaner. All these are extenuating circumstances."

"Yes, well, I've got all that down in writing. I did see the fitters' report," said Mr Franker.

"There are more extenuating circumstances," protested Jim

Simpson. "The G5 was also an unfit engine, its right injector clack was blowing. It was later replaced by another engine at Whitby. Further there was a doctor on the train who had to be got to Ravenscar to save the life of a mother with child. There were exceptionally deep snowdrifts at both the mouth of the tunnel and at the exit. At all costs the driver felt that he must get through the tunnel. He had already stopped on the line to raise steam. And finally the driver is the locomotive's captain, he is in command, the fireman has, at all times, to obey his driver." Jim paused and looked around his audience, "That's all I'm going to say." He began to gather his notes together, Joe looked nervously at Jim with a feeling that more needed to be said.

"You've both said quite a lot. We've noted it," said the locomotive inspector. "I'm making my way to Malton now to hear what Mr Coney and the Malton shed master have to say."

"Did you see the Whitby Gazette report about the snow ploughs and the babies?" asked Joe, pulling from his pocket a news cutting. "This arrived from a friend in Whitby this morning." The headline, 'Snow Ploughs Save Mother and Twins' immediately communicated its relevance. The public commendation of the actions of the L.N.E.R. staff, who took the doctor through the blizzard to Ravenscar and the mother and babies back to Whitby in spite of the mechanical failure of one of the locomotives, was received with pleasure by the group.

"Do you mind if I keep this for the General Manager to see?" asked the Inspector. Joe agreed. Then the Inspector asked, "What are you both on today?"

"I'm cleaning today at one o' clock," Joe stated.

"I'm on afternoon York," added Jim Simpson.

"By the way Mr Franker," informed Joe. "I've put a 'leave application' in for absence from Thursday so that I can go to Leatherhead with Dan West. I'll be back for work late shift on Monday next."

"Yes I know. I've just sent a note to the bottom shed for the running foreman to show you absent on the rosters for those days." Mr Franker paused, "I hope Dan West gets some good news."

Joe muttered his thanks and then left with Jim. "Thanks for all that Jim. You put up a good show for me. I wonder what happens next?"

"You'll get a letter in a day or two. Don't worry about it. Worrying won't help."

"I'd like to have known before I go to Leatherhead with Dan."

★ ★ ★ ★

3
Victory Day.

The ten-fifteen York train on platform three at Castlebrough was the objective of the small group around the ambulance at the entrance to the station. The wheeled stretcher-bed being extracted from the ambulance was on its way to the train, two porters were helping push the bed containing Dan West towards the front guards van.

Tom West was his usual ebullient self, moving about agitatedly and waving his arms, first moving in one direction and then reverting. He was agitated, his son Dan was embarking on a long journey to Leatherhead in Surrey, that was cause enough to justify his behavior.

Dan's mother and Joe were in the party, they were going with Dan to Leatherhead in Surrey on the journey that had been arranged on the Queen's suggestion. There was hope in their hearts that good news might await them at the Emergency Medical Services Hospital. Even though the papers were filled with urgent war news there was going to be a report in the Castlebrough Evening News about the local lad's journey of hope. Tom West had inspired that and had just completed a discussion with the reporter.

"Let's look at the loco Joe," the statement came from Dan.

"We've time, come on." agreed Tom West.

Unusually, there was a London Midland 'black five' loco to take them to York on the first leg of their journey and it provided a talking point for the crew and Dan. It was common practice for some passengers to view their train's locomotive and talk to the crew, Dan was no exception. Although his view of the locomotive footplate was limited because of his position on the mobile bed he showed the usual interest.

"We're changing trains at York. I could have gone by ambulance to York but I asked if we could travel by train," Dan elaborated for the reporter, "We've got to travel by train from York to London so I thought I'd travel by rail to York. I've got to do the last lap from Kings Cross by ambulance."

The journey in the front guards van was uneventful. Joe travelled with Dan and together they viewed the landscape through the single window while Mrs West and a nurse kept a watchful eye from a nearby compartment. The 'hearing' only two days previously of Joe's alleged transgression with the J21 formed part of their conversation about railways, the rest comprised the war, the post-war, and the pigsty building which might have to be postponed. The change of

On Trial

trains at York was smooth as was the ambulance journey from Kings Cross to the Leatherhead hospital.

Nearby lodgings accommodated Joe and Mrs West. The anticipated following day with its medical examination came around quickly. Joe and Mrs West had a meeting with the specialist and received the startling news, "God himself couldn't make that lad walk. He's lost ninety-eight per cent of his spinal chord and got two shattered vertebrae."

The knowledge produced tears in their eyes; they'd known it but hadn't want to believe it. When they heard it confirmed by a specialist with such simple brutality there was no room for doubt. It established the reality for all time.

The news was stated again to Dan in the long ward where he lay with war-wounded spinal-injury men. Dan's broad grinning face and wide nostriled nose recorded no complaint, disappointment or surprise. The doctor, cheerfully seated on the bed, talked of an operation that would ease the disablement and about suitable vocational training.

★ ★ ★ ★

Joe stayed at the hospital with Dan as long as possible, he extended his stay until early Sunday evening and then took a late train northwards to York from King's Cross. He aimed to join the 4 a.m. mail train from York to Castlebrough and arrive in plenty of time for his late Monday shift.

He journeyed home with a feeling of apprehension about the judgement that must have already been handed down and awaited him. The long train rolled through the dark night and threatened to lull its occupants to sleep with its rhythmic motion and its distinctive clopperty-clop of wheel against rail-end. It succeeded with Joe and he was only roused to action when he sleepily saw the York Station name board passing the window as his train slowly pulled out of York Station on its journey to Newcastle.

Joe leapt up in panic grabbed his suitcase, and shouted, "I've got to get off here." He pulled open the compartment door to make a hasty departure possible, the train was moving at an increasing rate but Joe considered himself to be skilled at leaping from moving trains; he had to get off, the next stop was Newcastle. He positioned himself and his case for the quick leap, but instead of his planned forward exit he fell backwards with indignity.

"Bloody fool! You'll kill yourself." A fellow traveller in the compartment had unceremoniously pulled him back from the brink. Joe had to grudgingly accept the judgement and wait until the train arrived at Newcastle, then catch the next train back to York to finally arrive in Castlebrough at twelve noon, just in time sign on for his next shift.

He looked in vain in the shed time office for his expected letter. He cursed, he wanted the result of the disciplinary hearing as soon as possible. There was no word, so with Driver Johnson and a D49 locomotive he collected fifty empty cattle wagons from the Sander Station cattle market siding and took them to York.

On his return to Castlebrough shed that same day Joe was relieved to see a sealed envelope on the chargeman's desk, he opened it with apprehension and his face fell as he noted the short message to 'Passed Cleaner Joseph Wade, Please see me on Tuesday morning at about 10.a.m to receive the result of the recent investigations into the failure of J21 engine number 1516. signed, F.Franker, Shed Master.' His blood ran cold and without a word he went home to a sleepless night. The morning came around with frightening speed but every second and waking moment took an age.

"Morning Joe," smiled and greeted Shed Master Mr Franker as Joe walked into his office, neatly and cleanly dressed, bent on creating a favourable impression. "Did you have a good weekend with young Dan West?" Joe replied affirmatively and tried to close the discussion on that particular matter. He just wanted the news about himself and the J21, only that would abate the sickness in his gut. "Let's go into my office, Joe."

The seconds were slow again, he could hardly breathe. "Yes," continued Mr Franker. "I thought I'd tell you rather than write to you. You're in the clear, no Form One, or Caution. Nothing on your record."

"How come?" Joe's head was in a dizzy joyous spin.

"The way you presented your side, and what Ted Coney said."

"What was that?" His demeanour was outwardly calm and did not reveal his inner turmoil.

"He insisted that he was in charge and he took full responsibility. He told you not to put the injector on until after you got through the tunnel."

"Is he in the clear or does he face discipline?"

"I can't tell you that. It's confidential. I can tell you one more thing, he said you were a bloody good fireman."

Joe's head buzzed with excitement as he walked down the shed yard where he saw Tom West oiling a V2 locomotive. Tom filled in the missing piece of news. "Ted Coney accepted all responsibility and a week's suspension with loss of pay."

"That's rotten," expressed Joe.

"Not really. That was the least he expected. You can't drop your plugs and get away with a written warning." Joe agreed. Tom continued his judgement, "You've got your first year firing shifts in haven't you? You've been baptised, you're a fireman now, on fireman's pay all the time."

"Aye! Some baptism!" exclaimed Joe. "Dropping me fusible plugs and ruining the engine, that don't happen to many first-year firemen, an' chuckin' the fire out and, and - -" He was just going to say and 'getting home by coast guard' but he remembered his vow to keep mum. "If I was getting my first year in at Ravenscar, it was some baptism, I reckon I've had a baptism of fire."

★ ★ ★ ★

Joe visited Dan and the war-wounded on a later occasion in May. He enjoyed the visit and the ward discussion, particulary about the proposed new welfare benefits, free medicines, and about the National Government's promised policy on maintaining full employment that had become the norm during wartime. Politics and change dominated conversation in the ward.

There was a spirit among these seriously wounded servicemen that Joe had never witnessed elsewhere. He heard a little about the actions that had reduced them from fit young men to war-wounded invalids, but he learned also of their determination to get on with their changed lives. He learned more about the course of the war, how it was about to end, of the reported death of Hitler, about concentration camps that were displaying their horrors to the world, and about the hope that a new social system would come into being and provide good housing, pensions, education and a welfare state. It sounded promising, exciting to Dan and Joe. They had a feeling of being present at a great moment in history.

That visit was notable because of the imminence of 'Victory in Europe Day', but it was also notable for another event. Joe's visit was a week-end hop to Leatherhead from Friday afternoon to the following Monday morning on his free travel pass in his uniform and overalls. At York he waited for his London bound train on platform eight in the company of York fireman Bob Hugston and his York driver. "You got a place on the Ruskin College Summer School I see," said Bob.

"Yes, July, I'm looking forward to that, thanks for drawing it to my attention. You won the Area Council election, I see. Congratulations." The short whistle blast of an approaching train drew Joe's attention to the London train approaching them down number eight platform, at it's head was the powerful streamlined A4 pacific locomotive No 4468.

"This one yours, Bob?" asked Joe then he followed Bob's answer, "Yes," with his own exclamation, "It's the Mallard!"

"Yes, it's ours to Peterborough where another crew takes over."

"The Mallard? The World's fastest? The speed record holder!" Joe couldn't believe it, he was going to ride behind Mallard to London unless - he nurtured the thought, 'I can ride on the footplate to London'.

The incoming crew handed over speedily, Joe climbed aboard without spoken permission, planted his small case on the fireman's seat and asked, "Is it alright if I have a look around?" He continued with excitement in his voice, "She did 126 m.p.h." Then he shut up about it and thought, 'I'll have something to tell Dan about if I can scrounge a ride on her'. The York crew were treating Mallard like any other working locomotive.

"Climb up there Joe, put the water-hose in the tank," instructed Bob Hugton pointing upwards across the tender to the water tank. "That'll help."

"We've got a passenger," the driver addressed his fireman Bob Hugton.

"Yes," Bob replied, thinking of Joe.

"Speak of them, they're there. You'll have to give up your seat Bob."

Bob followed his driver's gaze down the platform. Two men were advancing towards the Mallard.

"That's Loco Inspector Mike Smith," said Bob. "I wonder who the other guy is?"

"It'll be the new District Locomotive Superintendent who's took over Blanchard's job. I got wind that he might show up. He'll be travelling with us on the footplate." He grinned. "I'll have to ask for his pass. There's always someone who wants to hitch a lift on the Mallard."

"You can say that again Bob," responded Joe as he picked up his small case and disappeared quickly and quietly to get a seat on the train.

★ ★ ★ ★

Joe arrived in London and Leatherhead amid news about the surrender of Germany and the victory celebrations planned for May the eighth.

"You ought to go into London tomorrow, you two," said Feathers Starling to Dan and Joe from the next bed. "Big celebrations are planned, Doenitz surrendered Germany at 2 'o clock this morning. Tomorrow has been named 'Victory in Europe Day'. There are going to be big celebrations all over and especially in London."

"I can't go," said Dan. "I'm in hospital."

"But you can get in a chair, an' you can manage your water-works. Borrow a chair in the morning and just skate off to the railway station and don't tell anybody."

"Got to tell someone I'm going out, surely."

"Just going for a walk in the grounds, tell 'em. I'd go if I could get in a chair an' I had a mate to push me."

London was the tumultuous experience they expected. They'd made no provision for eating or drinking but they were feted everywhere; at street parties, in public houses with intoxicated crowds, and in the evening with the mighty crush on the Mall and outside Buckingham Palace, where swaying crowds howled "We want the King." They saw the King and the Queen and family, and Winston Churchill. Although they both considered themselves to be opposed to the institution of royalty they felt the psychological urge to shout and sway with the crowd, "We want the King." They couldn't resist, they became convinced royalists for the day, and why not, war was over at last.

1
Election Fever.

The shouting startled Joe, he'd just entered the large ground floor lecture hall in Roscoe Rooms with Julie Burton. They both displayed a little discomforture about their late arrival. The lecturer Bill Evans was stating a position on the civil war in Greece and why British troops were fighting E.L.A.S. Communist anti-Nazi forces in Greece. Something that he had said caused a storm of anger from a significant minority of the audience.

"It's sounds heated, I don't like too much controversy when I'm trying to learn," said Julie.

"What are we supposed to be learning?" asked Joe. "They're only talking about - no not talking, arguing about Europe."

"Political affairs, that's what we are learning about. There is always a lot of arguing in political affairs classes," replied Julie.

"Well I like it," responded Joe, "It excites me, it isn't like any class at my school."

"No it isn't. This is adult education, it's a University class. Bill Evans is a lecturer in International Relations," said Julie Burton proudly.

"Why do you want to learn in this class? You're a teacher."

"I've got to know as much as I can about everything. One of my pupils comes from the Caucasus and I - -. We'd better not talk. Shush. I'll tell you when we have coffee."

Joe was obedient. He noticed she'd asked him to have coffee and she was a teacher, he was just a coal shoveller. Lord, he'd found some elevated company. There was John Booth, a local head teacher, and also the Head of the Department of Secretarial Studies at the Municipal Technical Institute. A Muckle and Wragg's solicitor was there, and the President of Castlebrough Art Society, and so too was Major Huskisson from the Army Educational Corps. What was he getting himself into? He couldn't talk proper, he'd been left school for so long now he'd nearly forgotten his teachers names. He switched from his inner reverie at the shouted announcement by Bill Evans, "After tea break we'll examine the prospects facing us as a result of the resignation of the Churchill Government on May 23rd."

"That'll be interesting," said Joe, "though I won't be able to vote in the General Election. I'm not old enough." He reprimanded himself, he shouldn't have said that, he'd been keeping quiet about his age. Being young was a handicap, like being ignorant, and he was both. Why was he in this elevated company? Was that the right word? He'd better look it up. Maybe it was 'exalted company', that sounded even grander.

"Who do you think can best deliver the reforms that this country needs?" asked Major Huskisson of Joe. He had seated himself opposite Joe and was energetically dipping his two biscuits into his milky tea.

"The Beveridge Report, the restructuring of industry, and the creation of a free health service, those are the reforms I would want to see. Without a doubt, only Labour will deliver them." Joe was surprising himself. Was he really speaking these ideas?

"Are you a student?" the Major asked.

"No, an engineer. That's really the name for a locomotive driver. I'm training, I'm really learning to be a driver." Joe felt confident among them in his new brown utility suit from the Cooperative Stores and his hard white-starched collar, he felt something more than 'just a locomotive fireman'. His hair was caked in brylcreem and the front carefully pushed up into a wave and a flick. Only his spots detracted from the handsome image he hoped he conveyed to this exalted company.

"You answered that question like a student of politics would."

"I'd like to be a student and I'm interested in politics, everything's changing in the world, it's so interesting. I was reading about Democritus and his early theory about the atom. That led me to read about Albert Einstein's Theory of Relativity and the possibility of making an atomic bomb. I didn't really understand it though."

"Yes. Who does?" laughed the Major. "The times are changing dramatically, revolutionary really. There've been so many changes in the last ten years, it really is a time in which to be alive, that is if you can keep yourself alive. Millions have died, many millions, it's been the most devastating war in history, another Dark Age. But it's over, we're coming into the light now, we're going somewhere better."

Julie joined in with a devastating onslaught on war and forced them to discuss the Peace Pledge Union and the growing movement for peace.

Afterwards, Joe went out of his way to walk with her in the direction of her down-town room and small kitchen. "I've had an inspiring evening Joe, I've enjoyed it so much, and I'm so impressed by your inquiring mind. Have you time for a cup of tea?"

He had all the time in the world for this personable, attractive, intelligent young woman. He noticed more of her features, strong shoulder length chestnut hair, full lips and a laughing, intelligent face; tall, shapely figure, and eyelashes that were long and delicately curled. She did more to him than simply stimulate his interest in politics.

Julie interrupted the tea drinking and the flow of conversation and unexpectedly said, "You'd better go now Joe, I've a lot of preparation to do for school tomorrow." She rose from her chair and that action added an air of finality.

"I've really enjoyed this evening, as well as learning a lot," responded Joe.

"I have, too Joe. It's much nicer to go to the class with someone. Thanks." She reached out and took his hand, it electrified him, he went limp, then gripped her hand as though some message was passing between them. "Keep on studying Joe. It's so good to see someone trying so hard." She suddenly moved towards him and kissed him lightly on his right cheek. "Keep it up." She turned him towards the door and turned the handle, Joe was plucking up courage to kiss her in return but he was outside with her 'goodnight' ringing in his ears. Thoughts about her burnt into his mind on the long walk home, he'd completely forgotten about the last bus but it didn't matter. He wanted all the time possible to think about his 'teacher', he wanted to know more about her and he didn't have long to wait.

★ ★ ★ ★

Double British Summer Time had brought long light evenings at the end of April. The ending of strict blackout regulations two weeks previously and their replacement with 'a dim-out' still meant doing without street lights, but it seemed to help lift the gloom. Vegetation was in full leaf, the seafront at Castlebrough was taking on a pre-war holiday spirit, even though barricades and anti-tank defences were still in place but many of the marks of war had disappeared. The seafront was busy for early June, revealing that holidaymakers had already started populating the town.

Engine number 1445, the B16 locomotive that usually worked the town's daily coal train, was available for passenger working on Saturdays in June and it had been allocated to Joe and to Bob Laker, who had only weeks to work to reach his sixty-fifth birthday. "We've got a good un. This'll make short work o'er Enthorpe top. Have yuh been that way son? Bob asked." Joe had, the first time had been with Simpson and the bren-gun carriers and the hot big-end, the second was when he'd double-headed a long holiday train from Selby through Enthorpe and Bridlington to Castlebrough.

"What are we going that way for, Bob? It just says Butlin's Holiday Camp on the roster."

"It's a train to Birmingham from Filey with Butlin's Camp visitors. We take it via Market Weighton to Selby and bring another one back but keep our own engine."

The shed and the yard were busier now on a Saturday and Sunday than during the war, holiday trade saw to that. Every man was on duty and spare men were being borrowed from Malton and Pickering sheds.

"I've finished oiling, Joe. We leave from Londesborough Road Station at nine-forty to Filey Station where we pick up passengers for Birmingham. I'm going to the messroom, got an awful bad stomach, I'm going to take some hot water and bicarb."

Joe followed him to the messroom five minutes later, in twenty minutes they were due to leave the shed. He found unexpected activity.

"Better send for a doctor, Bill," shouted a voice. Joe heard the call as he neared the messroom. "Bob's poorly."

"Get an ambulance," shouted another unseen figure.

Alarm struck Joe, he broke into a run. It must be his mate Bob. The messroom door was ajar and a number of locomen were assembled around Bob who lay gasping on the sand-strewn messroom floor.

"We'd better get him up on to the table, help him to breathe."

"He won't be going with you Joe," said Bill Clarke. "Go and see if you can get Jack Burton to come down to be your mate, he's the only one left who knows the road to Selby."

Joe hated departing when his mate was ill and struggling to breathe. He'd had a soft spot for Bob ever since that first shift with him on the mainline to York during that raid. He ran up Harcourt Avenue to Fifty Bob's house and banged on the door. "It's me Jack," he shouted.

Joe banged again on the door, his urgency was apparent, the door opened and a female voice answered.

"Wait a minute." Julie Burton looked out. Joe's quick request for her father received the answer that he was in the bath.

"But we're stuck. My mate Bob Laker's been taken ill. Somebody's got to take his place."

"He's in the bath in the scullery," said Julie. "Go to the door and shout to him." She stood aside and gestured that Joe make his way towards the scullery door.

Joe's knock and call to Jack on the other side of the door resulted in Jack's blunt reply, "I'm in the tub, Joe, I can't come." Joe shouted the details of the emergency through the closed door.

"Open the door Joe and come in but don't let the street see me." Jack was in a large zinc bath in the middle of the floor, well lathered and submerged in steaming water. "I can't come to work now, they'll have to find someone else. Anyway what's up?" Joe explained that Jack's long-time friend Bob Laker was very ill. That set Jack on course to go down to the shed to see what was the matter. "I'll get dried and come down, but I won't be able to work Bob's train in twenty minutes."

"But bring your working togs Jack, just in case they can't get anyone else."

On Jack's suggestion, Julie Burton walked quickly down to the shed with Joe because she had been trained as a nurse and might be able to help Bob. The ambulance pulled up at the small shed-gate while Julie joined the prostrate Bob laid on the messroom table, a folded coat raised his head. Joe saw him from a distance, he was so still but Bill Clarke was talking quietly to him and rubbing his cheek. The door closed behind the stretcher bearers and within minutes they emerged and ran to the ambulance but Joe did not witness Bob's departure because he was making last minute preparations to engine 1445.

Jack Burton agreed to take Bob's place and he and Joe were a little late arriving at Filey seven miles from Castlebrough. The platform was packed with home-going campers, holiday-making was a new experience to most of them and only made possible by the end of the war in Europe.

The journey up the bank through Hunmanby and Speeton was a treat to the crew, the grasses were a bright lively green and Spring and early Summer blossoms were peeping. The ever numerous wild rabbits bounced in the fields at Hunmanby and disappeared into the tunnelled banks as the heavy train and pounding locomotive ruptured the tranquillity of their territory. 1445 steamed like a dream and lifted her exhaust steam and smoke over the train behind. No slipping wheels, no struggle to maintain the water level, just the steady pounding rhythmical beating of the exhaust. 'A joy to be at work,' thought Joe, 'and they pay me for it.' It was a joy that increased as they passed over the summit and coasted downhill through Bempton and Flamborough to thunder non-stop through Bridlington. Platform crowds waiting for later trains waved as they passed, Jack and Joe replied to the expression of greeting as was the universal practice of train crews and public. Jack sounded his engine whistle as they travelled through the station and saw all signals were at clear. He opened the steam regulator and re-activated the rhythmic beat at the chimney top. They gathered speed as they passed Bridlington locomotive shed and swung around the bend near Bridlington South signal cabin on the level track that would take them through Carnaby on towards Driffield.

"We'll be back on time when we pass Driffield won't we Jack?" shouted Joe with a gesture towards his pocket watch.

"Yes. She runs like a sewing machine," replied Jack. "Won't have any trouble up the bank to Enthorpe top." The footplate rocked steadily and rode smoothly causing Joe no difficulty with his balance as he confidently swung coal into the firebox.

They didn't have any trouble. Non-stop they sped through Driffield, and up the bank to Enthorpe, downhill to Market Weighton and through on to Selby where they detached their locomotive to allow another one take the home-going campers forwards to Birmingham. There was time to turn their engine, get water and have their sandwiches and bottled tea. Their train guard joined them while they awaited the Filey bound, train-load of fresh campers from Birmingham.

"Ought to have a red flag on the top lamp bracket," the Castlebrough guard said laughingly as he boarded the footplate for his lunch-break. "Labour should get in surely. And that'd please you Jack, wouldn't it?"

"Not half," replied Jack.

"Me too," added Joe enthusiastically. "Hope they nationalise the railways, if they do." He started a one-sided debate amongst the three of them. The guard was not sure about state ownership. Joe and Jack were very enthusiastic.

The guard changed the subject, "Pity about poor Bob Laker. He was due to work this train wasn't he?"

"Good job I could take over his job," commented Jack Burton.

"Bloody rotten luck for poor Bob. Just five weeks to his retirement and he has to go and drop down dead in the messroom at work."

"Drop down dead!" exclaimed Joe. He was taken to the hospital in the ambulance, wasn't he Jack?"

"Yes."

"Word was around at the station that he'd died," said the guard.

"I didn't know that, no one said he was dead. They took him to the hospital. He wasn't conscious when I saw him. That's all I know," Jack added as he sought to end the speculation on Bob's fate.

Joe was shaken, he liked old Bob, liked to share the footplate with him. He'd intended to go around to Bob's house on their return to Castlebrough, he'd still go, he had to know. He felt a personal loss, felt emotion arise in him, there was almost an urge to cry but that wouldn't do, he had a job to do. It was only an old friend who'd died, not like losing your Mam or Dad. But he hadn't died. Can't say he's dead just because somebody says that they've heard that he's dead. 'I'll have to wait 'til I get home,' thought Joe.

The day was now marred for Joe. The good engine, good weather, the delight he had felt about a forthcoming general election were all of less importance now. He had a definite feeling that Bob was dead. The Birmingham train arrived, they coupled to it and when the guard gave the necessary green flag signal they departed for Market Weighton on the way to Filey on the Yorkshire coast with their hopeful holiday-makers.

They were on time and making excellent progress on the level track through the country stations, and hoped for a good run through Market Weighton and on up the steep bank to Enthorpe. They would have to obey the 45 mile per hour speed restriction through the large country station at Market Weighton which was placed at the junction of four cross-country lines.

"All board's off at Everingham Joe. Next station's Market Weighton, soon know if we're going to get a run." Joe stooped to his firing task, ready for the hard blast to the top of the bank. He felt the thrill of the run. The sound of Jack using his large vacuum ejector to improve the trainpipe vacuum suddenly made Joe pause and look up.

"The brake's are going on. I'm shutting off, put your blower on," shouted Jack. Joe obeyed and watched the vacuum brake gauge needle register the fact that the brakes were slowly being applied. "Somebody must have pulled the communication cord. I'll overcome it so that we don't stop on a bridge. We'll have to stop quickly," he said as he slowed the train's speed. "You get off when you can and see if you can see a butterfly in the wrong position."

Down the side of the locomotive went Joe while it was still in motion. He dropped in running position from the moving train and turned when he stopped. He knew what the butterflies were, there was one high up, at the end of each carriage. He had to look at each vehicle to see if a butterfly could be found that had turned into vertical position. That would tell him whether the communication cord had been pulled and in which carriage. It was really the guard's duty to examine the train when the brakes had been applied but because of the direction of the train it was quicker for the fireman to seek the coach on which the brake had been utilised. It was the third coach from the engine, heads were already visible at its windows. Joe placed his hands and arms into a sudden upright position indicating to his driver that the train should be stopped immediately. "Here, pal," a Brummy voice called. The figure then opened the carriage door. Joe reached up and climbed onto the running board and entered the carriage.

"A lady in here. Needs help. She's going to have a baby her hubby says. Or she's ill."

Another man appeared. "My wife, she needs help. She's in agony, her baby's not due yet for five weeks."

"Is there anyone here that can help?" asked Joe. There wasn't. Somebody had gone for the guard. "Is she ill or having a baby?" asked Joe."

Her husband said he thought she was ill. She still had five weeks to go and she'd never had trouble with her other pregnancies. She had felt very well and ready for her holiday. "I want her to see a doctor," said the husband. "I think she's more ill than in labour."

"I'll put the brakes right and ask my driver to take the train to Market Weighton, that's not far away." He closed the butterfly valve and joined his engine. His message to Jack was urgent, and earned a quick response, they hauled their train quickly to Market Weighton.

The emergency was out of crew's hands. The lady in distress and her family were moved from the train to accommodation and medical help somewhere on the station premises. The train crew's duty was plain, they had to proceed with the train to Filey from a standing start at the foot of the 1 in 95 two mile climb to Enthorpe summit.

They were twenty minutes late and other trains behind them were likewise delayed, they did their best, up and over the hill, straining the B16 locomotive to its limit and going downhill as fast as the tracks and the speed restrictions would allow.

They were time-tabled throughout the journey not to stop until they arrived at Filey but they didn't expect a clear run on busy lines on a Saturday in June. To their pleasure and surprise they ran without a signal against them from Market Weighton to Driffield and then on to Bridlington and over Speeton bank to pull into Filey Station only five minutes late. Joe felt a sense of achievement as he saw the holiday campers leaving the train for the waiting buses that would take them to the newly opened holiday camp.

"Thanks pal," said the familiar Brummy voice that had addressed Joe when the train had stopped close to Market Weighton. "Looks like my pal's wife was going to have her baby, they were going to put her in the cottage hospital. The family went with her, wouldn't leave. Don't know what they will do. Anyway, thanks you two for what you did." Joe and Jack nodded their approval of the passenger's thanks, it was a pleasant part of their job to be addressed by satisfied passengers. The man rejoined his friends on their way to the holiday camp.

"Our Julie could've been some help there," said Jack.

"How come?" asked Joe.

"She trained as a midwife before she became a teacher. She'd a' bin useful at Market Weighton."

"She's clever ain't she Jack. Knows something about everything, politics, art, everything. She's pretty too. She doesn't take after you for looks Jack even if she's got your brains."

"I'm pretty, when I've got me Fifty Bob suit on," answered Jack lightly. "I'll have another bath when I get home and get me suit on."

"I'll find out about Bob."

"Don't expect too much, Son."

"Why?"

"I think you'll find out that the guard was right. Our Julie and the ambulance men said they were sure Bob was dead."

Joe didn't know how to react. He knew Jack had kept the news from him until he'd ended his day's work. Emotion swept through him.

★ ★ ★ ★

Joe's shoulder bone rubbed hard against the coffin bottom. Bob was quite heavy and the six bearers staggered as they carried him from the place that had been his home for so long. Joe was reminiscing, his mind rehearsing the scene when he'd first fired to old Bob on the mainline nearly two years ago and Bob hadn't wanted to take him. Joe could hear the old boy telling Franker that he wasn't 'going to take this young kid in the blackout'.

Joe had been pleased to have been asked to be one of the bearers at Bob's funeral, the tradition was that the man's union branch provided the bearers if the man's widow asked for them. Bob was an A.S.L.E.F. man and the other five bearers were A.S.L.E.F. Joe was N.U.R. and he'd been asked by A.S.L.E.F. because Mrs Laker had said, "Bob would have liked young Joe Wade to be one of his bearers."

The sombre procession to the grave side left Joe with time to think about Bob and the meaning of life. It saddened him to recall how Bob had worked so hard, yet acquired so little. Now he'd lost his retirement. Gone were his dreams of countryside holidays. The old-age state pension hadn't promised much and that was denied, and there was no company pension for ordinary railway workers. Fifty years he'd been a railwayman and only his work to show for it.

"He was going to get a watch from the L.N.E.R. for his fifty years as a railwayman. The vicar said that in his service address. You heard that didn't you Jack?" Joe spoke quietly now the party had retured to Bob's house.

"Yes I did. They never gave him one to time his trains by. Bob remarked on that only last week. 'They're givin' me one now I'm retiring so I can sit and count the minutes while I wait for my box', I heard him say."

"Yes," replied Joe as they left the house after a cup of tea, biscuits and condolences. He continued, "Some do all the work and others get all the pay. Bob used to say that. Why does it work out that way? Jack"

"I'll tell you," said Jack, "Capitalism, that's what puts one man in riches and another in poverty."

"You never miss a chance do you, Jack?

"No an' Bob wouldn't a' done either."

2
The Red Flag.

Johnny Marsay and Arthur Wilko were shunting the coal stage with a J94 saddle-tank engine, they had just been up the bank from alongside the shed to the high-level coal stage and brought down five empty coal wagons. They were now ready to replace them with four loaded coal wagons. A small red flag on a short stick fluttered from the front-top lamp bracket and sounds of the 'Red Flag' song of the Labour Party drifted from the engine cab.

Arthur, in full song with Johnny, pulled alongside the shed with the four loaded wagons. He reversed his engine and started the run at speed to climb the bank. A shed labourer held the points to turn the wagons and the engine towards the coal stage.

Joe, on his way to the shed to begin work found his attention drawn to the loudly exhausting engine as it started the run. He moved clear of the rails and continued to make his way towards the shed. The first wagon bucked as it moved over the points, the labourer holding the points handle staggered and let go as the wagon wheels left the rails. Arthur saw the danger from the careering wagon, he applied the engine steam brake instantly and all couplings tightened. Two of the leading wagons settled crazily on the sleepers and rocked, their wheel flanges splitting the points. The young shed labourer looked startled.

"That's the Red Flag for you." A loud voice carried from the nearby Sander Road. Johnny Marsay looked quizzically at the source of the voice, it was a man in overcoat and trilby hat, a man not unlike Franker. A middle-aged woman ranged on his arm but she contributed nothing to the anger expressed by her escort.

"Red flag Arthur, was there a red flag being waved?" shouted Johnny to his driver who'd halted the engine and wagons.

"No, what yer talking about? Nobody was waving a red flag. Stan just let the points go."

"This feller here, stood at the fence, is shouting about a red flag," replied Johnny Marsay.

Arthur Wilko stepped across the cab, "Who's he?" The man was merely gesticulating some concern or interest in the loco and the event. "I've more to do than talk to a member of the public. These bloody wagons is off." He left the footplate at the side away from the road to review the damage done by the derailment. Johnny followed him and again recorded the figure on the road saying something about the red flag.

Joe, on his way to work, on late shift, had seen Stan slip as he held the points in closed position, he saw the first two wagons lurch and bump onto the sleepers, then he joined Arthur and Johnny at the derailed wagons and contributed to the inquest.

"We'd better put 'em back on," said Arthur, "Wi' out getting a gang out and then we won't have to report it."

"I'll help. Will you want the tool vans bringing out?" asked Joe.

"They're at the bottom of six road. Should be able to carry enough jacks, chocks and ramps over here. There'll be some cleaners to help. There's that fellow up at the railings. He's saying something. Can you see what he wants Joe?" asked Arthur.

Joe ran up the steps from the shed yard and on to Sander Road where the trilby hatted figure and the female companion were observing the derailment. "Can I help?" asked Joe, "The driver asked me to ask you."

"I was just complaining about the red flag on the front of the engine."

"It isn't big enough is it?" responded Joe pleasantly. "They couldn't have a big one so near to the chimney it might have caught fire."

"It ought to be burned, all red flags. I mean. What do you think you're doing flying a red flag on one of my engines." The man was angry, that much was clear. Joe didn't see any significance in the man's puzzling complaint. He still responded lightly, "We've got red flags on all our engines."

The complainant spluttered, "Are you being cheeky? What's your name?"

"No, but we do have red flags on all our engines, Mister."

"You think you're going put red flags on Westminster and Town Halls. I know. You'll be a Labourite, all you railwaymen are the same. Well I'm going to do something about it. Tell me your name. I'm not having red flags being flown on engines that belong to me."

"I'm sorry Mister. I'm Joe Wade." Joe realised that the anger was real. "I don't know what you mean."

"We'll see about that, I'll have a word with the General Manager tomorrow." The woman on his arm was seeking to pacify him and move him away as he continued to speak angrily. "Messing about with the red flag, and singing the 'Red Flag' while working. That's what's derailed that wagon." Joe was spluttering short responses but he didn't interrupt the man's flow. "I'll see that this goes further. I'm a major shareholder. And I don't like all this talk about nationalising the railways. You'll hear about this from high up."

"I'm sorry Mister, I'll tell the driver." Joe walked away and made for the gate and the top of the steps. "I'll tell him, Mister."

He told Arthur Wilko that the man at the fence was grumbling about the red flag. Arthur nodded up to the drooping red flag at the chimney of his shunter. "Get that down Johnny. Who the hell put it up there?"

"I don't know," lied his fireman. "It was on when we picked up the engine."

"Loose off the first wagon, we'll try and get 'em on before Franker sees they're off." Arthur was actively organising the placing of oak and iron ramps at strategic places near the wheels.

"Won't the crane have to come out to get these on the rails?" asked Joe. "They must weigh twenty ton."

"We'll get them on in half an hour." Arthur turned to Stan, the labourer, "Get a hydraulic jack out of the van and jack that corner up far enough to get an iron ramp under the wheel. We'll have this wagon on in five minutes, there's only two wheels off." The engine pulled the wagon up the ramp and the wheels fell into place on the rails.

The leading wagon was completely de-railed, the four wheels were on the sleepers and the clinker ballast, it would not be so easy to pull up the ramps but it yielded slowly to the jacks and the heaving of the loco. The foremost wheels were hauled on to the rails and then a new strategy to deal with the trailing wheels lifted and coaxed them on to the tracks.

"Go and get a platelayer and a rail gauge to check that the track's are okay," Arthur instructed his mate. Soon they were driving their re-railed coal wagons up the bank and on to the coal stage.

Joe had learnt something about how to re-rail wagons without reporting through official channels that it had happened. He was surprised at the ease with which they had accomplished the task without sophisticated lifting equipment. The red flag had been removed from the lamp bracket after Arthur had heard Joe's report about the angry L.N.E.R. shareholder at the railings. There was nothing Arthur could do except tell Johnny Marsay off in a jocular vein about flying the red flag. Joe was due to report for work at 2 p.m. for engine cleaning, but he was late. Bill Clarke let him know about it.

"Late again Wadey. Funny how you're alus late and you just live across the road." He dismissed Joe's explanations with, "Go and get 2756 on the pit in No 1 road with Jim Woodley, Do some work in the dusthole for a change an' see if you can keep out of trouble. Show young South how to go on." Alf South was a recent recruit to

the shed's force of engine cleaners, he was not passed to act as
fireman so in time-honoured fashion he could learn something
about the fireman's craft by helping to stable or prepare engines.

"We've got to stable 2756, a D49 loco. We get an hour and ten
minutes allowed for this type of engine," Joe was explaining as he
walked with Alf from the stores. "This is rosalex hand cream I'm
rubbing on my hands. It's issued, helps to keep your skin free of
dermatitis. Makes 'em easier to wash."

Alf wasn't listening. He was excited by the presence of so many
locomotives. "Big as 'ouses, aren't they?" he commented excitedly
peering up to the locomotives occupying the adjacent road in the shed.

"Yes and that's only a J27, about 85 ton I think. Wait while you see
a Green Arrow or an A4. When did you start?"

"Only yesterday. Didn't expect to be firing today."

"You ain't," corrected Joe. "I'm the fireman. You're helping me."

As they emerged from the loco shed in the vicinity of the D49
locomotive Jim Woodley grumbled, "Where yuh bin? Yuh was due on
at two. We've six engines waiting for us to get on with. Ankler's on
at three for this one so get your skates on. Turn, watter an' coal her
first. Get goin' now, the way's clear." Joe tried to explain to Woodley
that he was late because he'd helped Arthur Wilko to put the coal
wagons back on track but he was waved on impatiently. "Don't you
learn any bad habits from him, kid." Jim addressed young South then
turned to Joe, "Turn me onto the table first and don't drop me off the
road at the points."

Joe sensed the excitement in young South as they jointly pushed
the manually operated turntable around. "Yuh wouldn't think me and
you could move hundred tons would you Joe? And with Jim riding in
the cab." After they had filled the tank at the water crane Jim Woodley
asked, "Are you alright for taking it back to the coal stage, if I turn
you in and then set the road?"

Of course he was, he felt exceptionally experienced with young
South riding on the fireman's seat picking his brains for railway
wisdom. He instructed the newcomer as he drove the engine down the
shed yard and placed it over the inspection pit, "You've got to apply
the brake gradually, especially when you're pulling up on greasy rails,
or she'll pick her wheels up and skate off."

"He's up there," Joe heard Jim Woodley shouting to someone.
Franker was moving towards the loco which Joe had just driven down
from the coaling point.

"Come down here Joe, Mr Franker wants you," shouted Jim.
Joe climbed down from the cab closely followed by young South.

He wiped his oily hands on a sponge cloth, felt conscious of the filth he'd acquired and shaped up to Jim Woodley and the shed master.

Mr Franker was not a man to strike fear into anyone but neither did his manner encourage insubordination, his general disposition was one of friendship and an expectation of mutual respectability. He looked straight into Joe's eyes, clearly putting him on the spot. "Who do you work for?"

"Well," Joe wondered to what the question was leading. "The L.N.E.R. I expect. Unless the answer is, I'm working for m'self at the end of the day."

"I thought so, you don't know do you?"

"The London and North Eastern Railway. That's who I work for, I thought it was trick question."

Franker came back with, "I thought maybe you worked for the Labour Party. Or for Russia."

"What!" exclaimed Joe.

"I've had a complaint about you. From high up."

"From God?" interfered young South as Joe's stomach lurched.

Joe hadn't been expecting any complaints, "I haven't done anything."

Franker withered Alf South with a look and addressed Joe, "That's not what I've heard. An important shareholder of the Company has complained to me about you. He said you flew a red flag from your engine and gave him a lot of cheek when he complained."

"It wasn't my engine and I didn't put a red flag on any engine. I don't know what he's talking about."

"He says you gave him cheek about having red flags on all engines."

"Yes, I did but we do have red flags on all our engines." Joe felt as though he was not doing his case any good. "I wasn't being cheeky."

"In the lockers, not flying from engines," Franker stressed.

"That's what I meant. Anyway Mister Franker I didn't put a red flag on any engine. I don't know who put that red flag on the saddle-tank while it was shunting. I didn't."

"How did he know your name?"

"He was waving from the fence. I just went to see him to see what he wanted."

"You gave him your name?"

"Yes, because he asked. I wasn't being cheeky. I didn't know about the red flag on the shunter. When I went back and told Arthur Wilko he got mad and had the flag taken down. Nobody knew how it got on the lamp bracket. It certainly wasn't me."

"You must have been bloody lippy."

"Honest. No, I wasn't."

Franker said "I'll have to see Arthur Wilko. The shareholder said a wagon was off the rails."

"Only a bit. They pulled it back on ever so quickly. Arthur will be at home now."

"The man is a shareholder, big enough to have the General Manager's ear. If I can't mollify him he's going to formally lodge a complaint on Monday morning. I'm going to give him your name and age and tell him you've apologised profusely. You didn't put the flag on the engine did you?"

'Mollify' and 'profusely', two new words that Joe would have to learn. He had to know what he was doing profusely. "Yes, sorry. I didn't mean I put the flag on, I meant I apologised profusely."

"I'll try and pacify him, but if I don't you'd better expect to hear more from up on high. An' I don't mean the Pope."

Joe nodded and said, 'Thanks,' while making a mental note to check up on the meanings of 'pacify' and 'mollify'. He excused himself with another 'Thanks' and went off with young South to complete their work on their remaining engines. His confidence returned and he spent a bit of time explaining how he'd got away with it. "Who do they think we are? A bunch of serfs? Just because he's got shares in the railway. Well, he won't have soon cos we're going to nationalise the railways."

★ ★ ★ ★

By coincidence Joe and Jack Burton were booked to work the Saturday holiday special for Butlin's camp from Filey to Selby for Birmingham. They were again allocated the B16 engine 1445. The memory of the previous Saturday morning and the death of Bob Laker was heavy in Joe's mind as they stopped their train on the up line platform at Filey. The platform was full of holiday makers, but two bus loads were still awaited from the camp. The train could not occupy the mainline platform for a lengthy period without holding up other traffic. Joe waited impatiently while Jack spent the time persuading him to help the local Labour Party with canvassing.

"Julie will be canvassing with you," Jack said. Joe felt more interested when he heard that, but he still had to wrestle with his conscience. The question of whether he should help a moderate Labour Party was paramount in his mind. There were many revolutionary movements in the world competing to attract the attention of newcomers to the political struggle. Joe felt enticed by the idea of a society that put power and money into the hands of working people, probably because he was a product of mining families, and their demands and sufferings had helped shape his ideas.

"Look Jack. There's the man whose wife was having the baby last Saturday. He pulled the communication cord."

"They're coming this way," added Jack. "The porter's kept a front compartment for them."

"That's the Mother in a wheel-chair, she's got a baby on her knee. Can I go and find out how things turned out for them?"

The family recognised Joe and explained how Butlins had arranged to fetch them by road from Market Weighton after the baby had been born. Butlins had made it possible for them spend their planned holiday in the camp. "The cream on the cake," said the father and the children in a gaggle of voices was that they had won the 'Happy Families' and the 'Mother and Baby' competition and they would get a free family holiday in August.

The baby had been born shortly after they had left the train. Joe felt infected by their good fortune and he recalled on the death of Bob in the mess-room on the same day as the birth of the little boy. Joe was about to leave and say goodbye to the family when the mother said, "Can I have a bit of clean coal for Robert to hold in his hand?"

"Clean coal," laughed Joe "There isn't such stuff. Who's it for?"

"Robert."

"Robert, - the baby!" exclaimed Joe. He noted the mother's nod. "Bob, you're going to call him. Good. I'll get a piece of Bob's coal for Bob." He climbed high on the tender where the coal had remained undisturbed for a long time. He selected an appropriate small piece, washed it under the tap on the tender and placed it in the baby's hand. "A piece of Bob's coal for Bob." He explained to the family about Bob.

When Joe left Jack at the end of the day he had pledged himself to attend a meeting of the Labour Party at the Public Library on Monday evening and to canvas support for Labour in the coming general election. "Do your bit for the workers. Don't just talk."

Julie Burton was there and so was Joe. She was also at the 'Current Affairs' class on the Tuesday evening and was becoming an attraction to Joe. She made him feel important, she focussed his attention on her and things that troubled him ceased to matter. He found that he was beginning to accept her ideas when she spoke in the discussion at the class. She was very moderate and a pacifist, maybe a Quaker, Joe considered. He sided with her when her contributions were derided by the more socialist members. After the class he walked home with her and together they commented on the beauty of the warm summer evening and the very obvious thrill of seeing street lights on after the years of the war.

"I can't remember the lights on in the streets before the war. I was twelve when the war started and didn't go out on an evening. It seems to me that there had never been lights on ever. It had always been dark." 'Damn it' he cursed to himself, 'I'm on about how bloody young I am.' "Do you care for poetry?" he asked Julie by way of altering the conversation. Of course she did, and she went on about poetry in such a way as to expose his ignorance and his lack of comment.

"Are we going to have tea?" he asked bravely as they approached her flat door. Over tea they found themselves talking about Bob and what had happened last Saturday. Joe sensed it was the wrong subject. "Tell me about yourself Julie. You've achieved such a lot." She did but she didn't mention her age or anything personal about her life. Joe was going to have to wait for that.

"I've had a lovely night with you," he said as she went to open the door. She agreed, Joe took her hand like she had done to him last time he had stayed for tea. It was limp and unresponsive. He grasped it more firmly, then he leaned forward and gently kissed her cheek. He felt his lips on her warm cheek and its touch against his nose, his free hand came up to her shoulder and her scent became more noticeable. Swiftly she responded, pushing Joe away firmly but gently, "It's time you went."

"But it's not late."

"It's too late to have you here. I'm a married woman, and twelve years older than you," she wasn't angry, just firm.

Joe felt shattered, he felt such a fool, his confidence was with the butterflies in his stomach. He opened his mouth but nothing came. She broke the developing silence, "I'll see you at the class next Tuesday. That's the last one for this session. Anyway there's going to be enough canvassing to do. The General election is on the 7th of July." She smiled at him. 'Was she laughing, or just trying to soften the blow?' thought Joe. "And my husband comes home next week on demob leave." Joe left after a few neutral phrases and briefly telling her that the woman on the train last Saturday had had a little baby boy called Bob and had won a free family holiday. He bade Julie goodnight and tried not to leave an impression that he had his tail between his legs.

He walked home in the company of his thoughts. God! What had he been thinking of? She was a teacher and 'he was only a locomotive cleaner'. He could have been in her class when he left school four years ago. He felt a great sense of stupidity, he'd been shown the red flag and had a red face to match.

3
Gun Fever.

The notice-case in the messroom displayed the 'Minutes of the Local Departmental Committee' signed by Franker for the railway company and by Tom West as secretary for the men.

"Really there should be a bath or a shower. Hot water and a couple of wash-basins isn't enough for a hundred and five loco shed staff," Rob Hibson commented after reading the proposals to improve washing facilities at the shed.

"Not much better than what we have now," agreed Joe.

"What's that?" asked young South.

"That stone sink in the shed corner with a cold tap. Do yer mean yer ain't been getting washed?" asked Hibson.

"I get washed in a bucket of hot watter on an engine, thank you," said Alf South.

"The craphouse is going to be altered," added Rob Hibson. "Instead of sitting alongside each other for a crap we're goin' to have three separate cubicles."

"Ain't that just luxury. Do we get toilet paper or Bloomer's 'Daily Worker'?" asked Mason, the fourth person in the messroom.

"Do you think this place is the Ritz?" Joe added as part of his contribution to the light hearted interchange.

"Don't be bloody greedy. You're going to get two washbasins, an' a gas water-heater, and three individual, cosy, little sound-proof crap houses." Hibson continued, "What more do you want? Bloody beds, if I knows you lot."

"What about cushions in the messroom?"

"And a games room where we can play cards without having to keep an eye open for Clarkey or Franker."

"Bigger wage packets and smaller shovels."

"That's just what Labour's going to do for us," added Joe.

"Let's have our snap and a game of cards."

"Not me," declined Joe, "Some of us 'as got work to do. I'm on York goods with Fifty Bob."

"Just a few hands, we need you to make up a four-some. A few hands of pontoon while it's quiet. It's our mealbreak, so Clarkey can't grab the kitty," insisted Rob Hibson.

The four of them settled at one of the two long tables. Cigarettes, sandwiches and tea accompanied the grubby pack of cards. The windows had been scraped clean of the thick blackout paint and the morning sun fell into the sand-carpeted messroom. A very small fire burnt in the large fire-grate to heat the kettle and provide for tea and washing. Rob Hibson carelessly tipped a handful of coins on the table and mischievous hands sought to claim a share of the rolling coins.

"Off, get yer bloody hands off." Hibson's right hand grabbed to rescue the coins from thieving hands and his left plunged into his khaki haversack on the seat alongside. "Put it all back. Or else." His left hand came into view with a German luger pistol in its grasp.

"Where yuh got that from?" asked Mason.

"Never mind. Just cough up wi' my money or you three's gonner play Russian Roulette."

"I'd like to see that," tittered Alf South.

"Is it loaded, Rob?" asked Joe.

"Course it is. There's some more shells," he replied and placed some live rounds of ammunition on the table. "Just keep the safety catch on and it's safe." He pointed the gun down the length of the mess-room. "I'll just put a bullet into Fifty Bob's locker." He pulled the trigger and all his company fell away. "Pow, Pow, Pow." Then he laughingly made a pretend attempt to put the pistol to young South's head but everybody scattered. "Shouldn't do that really. That's how accidents happen," he conceded. He fielded the questions about the origin of the gun, and what he was going to use it for. "I've shot rats with it in our kid's pigsty. It's a bit noisy though."

"There's a rat in the fitter's shop in the rat trap," informed Alf South. "Jim Munster was trying to spear it with a file tang."

"Are we going to have a game of pontoon?" asked Joe, feeling decidedly uneasy and at some risk.

"Let's see you shoot that rat," requested South who was displaying a feeling of hero worship for the reckless Rob Hibson.

"Let's go and look, this game of cards isn't going to take off," agreed Rob. The sneck on the mess-room door rattled and the door started to open. The gun disappeared from view.

"You lads on your meal-break?" asked night foreman Bill Frobisher. He was ready to go home at the end of his night shift. Bill Clarke and Tom West accompanied him.

"It's time you cleared out of here. It's past your twenty-minute meal break," stressed the chargeman Bill Clarke. "Come on! Clear out! We've got something to do in here. You stay Hibbo. We want a strong lad."

"Do you want me to stay as well?" asked young South.

"I said, a strong lad. You go off somewhere and tire yourself out shovelling feathers."

"I'm not cleaning this morning, Bill. I'm on York goods wi' Fifty Bob."

Joe was distancing himself from the lowly cleaners. He grabbed his haversack and jacket from the seat and made his way to his C6 locomotive in the yard.

Fifty Bob Burton was on the footplate reading the 'Daily Herald'. "Election results expected today," he said. "We'll soon know if Churchill's mob is going to be kicked out."

"Been a long time since voting day on July 7th," said Joe as he placed his clothes and haversack in the locker on the tender. "Hasn't it Jack?"

"That's been because they had to organise the vote for service men all over Germany and the Far East, all over the world. An announcement is expected this afternoon."

"I haven't voted. I'm too young and yet I could be in the forces at my age," added Joe as Jack removed the engine hand brake and they made off to collect their train at the goods yard.

"We've got a lot on today," said Jack Burton as they emerged tender first with their big express locomotive from Gallows Close tunnel and saw the length of their train.

"A lot of wood," responded Joe.

"That's what Gabriel Wade and English are buying in for post-war building," he explained. "It's to be stacked at Heslerton and Weaverthorpe."

They shunted where necessary at Sander Station on both sides of the large country station and junction that connected the Hull line, the York line and the Pickering line. They arrived at Heslerton to be put inside the yard after shunting to allow the up line 10.15 a.m. York express from Castlebrough to pass them on its way to York. Memories of the derailment with Bill Ankler and the delay of the up line York express two years earlier were refreshed in Joe's mind, as was the 'Whistle Stop' and 'Thistle Top' saga and Signal Woman Laura. She was on duty in the signal cabin so Joe devised an excuse to go and visit her. He couldn't use the 'carrying out Rule 55' as a pretext because their train was securely contained in sidings.

"Do you mind if I go up to the cabin Jack? I've got a couple of turnips promised." He couldn't just say, 'I'm off,' like he would to some drivers. He had to be careful how he treated Jack, he was 'a different kettle of fish', he followed rules and protocol. What's more, Jack might know that Joe had tipped his cap at his daughter and been rebuffed. Jack must not be rubbed up the wrong way. For good measure Joe added, "I'll see if I can get some boiling water for my billy can." He collected his dirty khaki haversack from the locker. "I might have time to eat a sandwich."

"Don't be missing when the board comes off after the express goes through."

Laura greeted Joe with a smile as he walked into the cabin. "I'm not going to be here much longer," she said straight away. "I'm glad you could get in, I'm going to a technical institute to do a secretary's course. I've decided that I'd like to work in an office." Joe seated himself on the form near the coats, assuring himself that he wasn't laying back on a coat that belonged to Laura. The kettle was boiling. Joe undid his haversack to get his tea leaves and sandwiches but was shocked into silence, Rob Hibson's luger pistol rested amongst his sponge cloths, books, papers and sandwiches. He fingered it without withdrawing it from the bag, it was real, not a figment of his imagination.

"Have you got any turnips, or anything else to sell?"

"The new ones are not ready yet, but I've got some carrots and broad beans, and cabbage."

"Okay." Joe couldn't think about anything but the luger, he didn't want it to become common knowledge that he had a live luger at work, in a signal cabin, and on his locomotive. He knew that Fifty Bob would be appalled and would declare it immediately, probably dump it in a rain-barrel for safety. There'd be some difficult questions and Rob Hibson might disclaim any knowledge of it and leave Joe as the worried owner of an illegal firearm.

"Are you not well Joe? You're very quiet."

"I'm alright. Got a terrible headache that's all. An' I'm hungry."

"Get your sandwiches then, you've time."

"I've got to go back on the engine, I'll just pay you for the vegetables. I'll see you another day, before you leave for technical school." He went back to join Jack, he was relieved he had because the guard had discovered some shunting to be done and Jack didn't like his fireman to be absent when the engine had to move.

"What are we doing with all this timber? It's unusual having all this at a countryside station, Jack?"

"It's being stockpiled by Gabriel Wades and the Government for building in this area. It's being stored at suitable country stations."

The wagons were being unloaded and the timber stacked in open spaces in the yard. Joe viewed the crossed timbers and wondered whether he could visit the stacks and drop the gun in one of the cavities within a stack. It wouldn't be found until the timber was used and by that time it would not be traceable to him. He dismissed the plan because there were too many curious eyes. The York express shot past and made the ground shudder and as soon as it passed

Heslerton's advance signal permission was given for Jack and the C6 to move out onto the mainline as far as the advance signal. Soon they were on their way to Knapton and Malton and more shunting.

They pulled into Malton and were pleased to see that the goods from York was waiting for them to exchange crews. Joe was increasingly nervous about the luger pistol in his haversack. He had to transfer the pistol, his vegetables, his coat and tea can, onto the York engine, and ensure that no one learnt of the possession in his haversack.

"Hand your things down chum, I'll hold 'em for you while you climb down." The York fireman had seen Joe struggling with his possessions. He took the haversack from Joe. "It's heavy. What you got in it, potatoes?"

"Yes," replied Joe. He scrambled down the cab side onto the ballast and claimed the haversack. He'd had nervous visions of the fireman dropping it and the gun discharging from the shock.

He wasn't pleased to learn from Jack that their change-over York loco was in Malton locomotive shed having a repair completed. "The drive arm on the mechanical lubricator is detached," said Jack. "It won't take long for them to fix it." It took too long for Joe, he was seated in the messroom with the luger pistol in the haversack. He was determined not to let anybody acquire it by mistake, just as he had from Rob, who must have mistakenly placed it in Joe's haversack.

★ ★ ★ ★

"You've got a lot with you Joe," said his mother.

"Just a few veg. for you Mam. I've got some tools here to put in the shed, they're for Tom West."

"Put them in the coal-house," came his mother's counter proposal.

"The garden shed'll do," replied Joe leaving through the back door grasping his haversack. He knew that he couldn't leave the gun in the shed for long, his father was home and working in Castlebrough and he used the shed quite a lot.

No one mentioned the luger until two days later when Rob referred to it quietly to Joe. "If anyone asks you if you've seen that luger. For God's sake say nowt about it. The police are looking for it. It's been used in a hold up somewhere. They've been to our house asking questions, they said I had been seen with a luger, I denied ever having seen one. You do the same."

"But Rob. . ." Joe paused.

"Eh! What?" asked Rob.

"But you had one."

"I didn't, and you can't prove it."

"What happened to it?"

"Somebody pinched it, that day in the mess-room." Rob looked quizzically at Joe, "I don't want to know what happened to it. You don't either. We've never seen it. I haven't, I don't know about you. But you haven't seen it if you've any sense."

Joe couldn't help but agree, he had to keep it to himself. Then he thought, 'That's just what I'm doing. Keeping it to myself quite literally'. When he went home the pressure was on him again, his father was clearing the garden shed. Joe had to be quick. He told his dad that there was a cup of tea waiting for him in the scullery and while his dad was absent Joe placed the gun in his haversack and went indoors to apologise for thinking that Mam had said there was a cup of tea.

The gun became a regular companion and frayed his nerves dreadfully. He daren't destroy it because it would be valuable evidence to the police and it would be a crime to dispose of it. He hardly dare let his haversack out of his grasp, then he saw a chance. Troops were lined up on number one platform waiting for an empty train to arrive for them to occupy. Joe and his mate on the station pilot were told to bring the train from Gas Up sidings for the troops. Joe climbed aboard the empty train and placed the luger under a seat, it would be found by carriage cleaners after the trip. Surely someone would believe that a soldier had hidden it.

Two days later Joe was ordered to Franker's office. "There was a luger in the messroom last Friday and you were in there," said Franker. "We know there was a luger because someone saw it and they said you were there."

"What's a luger?" asked Joe convincingly.

"You don't know what a luger is? Bloody hell and there's a war on."

"There was," said Joe.

"There still is," emphasised Franker.

"Sorry, you're right. I was thinking of the war against Germany."

"I'm answering, I mean, blast you, I'm asking the damned questions." Franker paused to calm himself, "What shift were you on last Friday. You were with Hibson and South on cleaning."

Joe pulled out a diary. "I keep my firing shifts in here. Last Friday I was with Jack Burton on the pick-up goods to York."

"You can be frustrating. Did you see a German army luger pistol in the messroom on that day?"

"No."

"Did you see any bullets, live ammunition lying around?"
"No."
"You should have because we found some."
"But I wasn't there."
"Bill Clarke, said he saw you in the messroom with other cleaners."
"I was firing to Jack Burton. I only went into the messroom to my locker when we'd prepared our engine."
"Okay, I'll believe you. It's just that whenever there's any trouble your name crops up. There's that matter about you being lippy to that shareholder and saying that all our engines should carry red flags."
"I didn't."
"Whether you did or not I'm issuing you with a 'Form 1' for attitudes unbecoming a railway servant."
"Oh! You can't Mister Franker."
"I can, and I'm going to. That's the only way I get York H.Q. off my back. Go on. Clear off."

Joe cleared off to the bottom shed and the messroom. He felt furious at the injustice Franker had visited upon him but the excitement amongst some enginemen in the messroom infected him.
"Labour's won, Joe. That'll bring in some changes," said Johnny Marsay expressing some of the optimism felt by most of those present.
"Won the general election do you mean?" asked Joe.
"Yes. With 200 hundred seats more than the Tories. A blooming landslide."
"Yes, forward the workers," grinned Alf South punching his clenched fist into the air as a sign of victory.
Rob Hibson intervened, "Hope it isn't an armed revolution, Joe."
Joe didn't respond, he'd had enough concern about Hibson's luger to dampen any enthusiasm he might have had for guns,
"They found the gun Joe," whispered Hibson in Joe's ear. "It turned up on a troop train from here to Birmingham. Franker told Tom West and then questioned us to see if there was any truth that there was a gun in the shed last Friday. Somebody must have talked."
"Mebbe it was you Rob. No one else knew anything about it. It was your gun," said Joe.
Rob took Joe to the corner of the messroom, "But I shoved it in your haversack when Frobisher came in."
"Can't have done. I never saw it again." Joe moved away towards his friend Johnny Marsay leaving Rob Hibson to puzzle over his fate. Joe would be pleased if the gun was never referred to again.

1
Poetry In Motion.

The York parcel train comprising fish and parcel vans and two passenger coaches drew to a halt opposite Castlebrough parcels office. It wasn't an important train, it stopped at all open stations on the line from Castlebrough to York in both directions but hardly ever carried any passengers. The York crew on the K class locomotive knew that the train was scheduled to run for only a few months more. The needs of war had kept it in use. The fireman uncoupled the train from the engine and climbed aboard his locomotive.

"Are you feeling any better now we're here Ron?" asked the driver of his fireman.

"It took me all my time to get the coupling off and get back on the platform," Ron replied. "If this pain don't ease I don't know how I'll get back to York."

"Do you think that you could drive back and I'll do the firing?"

"That might be possible. Oo!" yelped Ron. "It's so sharp, it creases me. Oo! oh! it's excruciating Bob." He made an effort to calm himself. "I'll be alright. Must be wind," he grimaced.

They both waited for the train's load to be stacked on four-wheeled barrows and taken to the parcels office, the fish stage or the milk stage. The few passengers who had missed the early morning mail train from York, or had joined the train at one of the country stations, emerged sleepily onto the platform. Milk cans, empty or full, bicycles, post office mail bags, empty fish boxes, parcels and cases, even a crate of squawking pigeons and a ticketed dog on a leash came forth from the old carriages. The train was due to return to York with the same engine and crew, they had first to travel to the shed for turning and refreshing the engine.

The K class loco slowly followed the drawn train down the platform. The fireman doubled up again and this time he fell on his knees. His mate Bob halted the engine and went across to him. "You can't go on like this Ron, you're not well. Sit on the step."

"I can't work like this Bob, you'll have to get another fireman. I'll have to see a doctor as soon as I get home."

"We'll get a doctor now."

"No. The pain will have gone when he comes. Just let me rest somewhere." He retched but did not vomit, he was sufficiently steady to insist on Bob taking the engine to the locomotive shed.

★ ★ ★ ★

"Bloody August and cleaning in the shed," grumbled Alf South over Frank Sutton's shoulder. They were cleaning the internal motions of an A8 tank locomotive so that the fitters could dismantle them for repair. "Never get my first year's firing in with things so slack."

"They're only slack 'cause you are down at the bottom of the list," responded Joe. The four of them in the engine's innards were at work with paraffin cans, rags, scrapers and the naked flames of their torch lamps.

"I alus feel like a miner down here digging and scraping. Not a very scientific job is it?" Alf moaned on, underlining the fact that he was bored.

Frank Sutton could be heard talking to Joe on another matter, "Rusty Iron's a real hard case, a nutter, but I don't think he'll really harm you Joe." Frank was comforting Joe after giving him the news that red-haired Rusty was looking for him but he was doing nothing to ease Joe's anxiety. "His brother said that you insulted his girl friend by asking her if she was on the game."

"No I didn't Frank. I'd said to young Wilko, would he join our game? But Rusty Iron's girl friend thought I was talking to her and had asked if she was on the game. Damn, hell, I'd never say anything like that. Trouble is everybody was too drunk. We just happened to be near 'Black Friars' and it's got a name for pro's. I wasn't looking for trouble, we were just on the way to Hell's Kitchen for a game of snooker."

"Young Iron, Scrap Iron you might know him as, he's stirring it up. He wants to see his brother put the frighteners on somebody," said Alf.

"He's succeeded. Tell him I've got the frighteners."

"Young Iron's put it about that you're a bit of a boxer so he's getting his brother to sort you out."

"O' Lord, I can't box kippers. I gave up playing at that mad pastime last summer.

"Whose the top cleaner this morning?" asked Jack Mild, the shed steam raiser, popping his head between the wheels of the A8 tank locomotive.

"I am," replied Joe Wade. "Why?"

"Frobisher wants you for a job. The fireman on the York parcels is too poorly to work his train back."

"Tell him I'll go, for nowt. Just to get away," interrupted Alf but he was ignored.

"That's good," replied Joe thoughtlessly and departed with alacrity towards the store.

"Go to York with Bob here, on the York Parcels train," instructed night foreman Bill Frobisher indicating in the direction of Bob, the stocky weather-beaten York driver. "His mate is proper poorly, he's going back on the cushions. You fire to Bob here, and pick up a travel warrant at York and come back on the cushions."

The instruction was a relief for Joe, not only was he bored with the cleaning job but his fellow cleaners were enjoying his discomfort over Rusty Iron's threat. He joined the York driver, Bob, in the messroom after washing some of the dirt from his hands and face. The morning sun blazed in through the windows of the neatly sanded messroom. 'Engine cleaning is a disgustingly dirty job,' he reflected.

Ron Templeman, the York fireman was stretched out on the long messroom seat, trying not to moan and groan. If he complained he would earn the advice that he should be seen by a doctor. He was adamant that he wanted to get to York first. Departure time arrived. After an uncomfortable ride on his locomotive's footplate with Joe and the driver back to the station, he stretched himself out on the seat of a non-corridor compartment close to the locomotive.

The station and the lines were very busy as the day prepared for a growing volume of traffic which comprised mostly of holiday makers taking advantage of the first peacetime summer since 1939. The war in the Far East against the retreating Japanese armies still continued violently, American bomber fleets pounded Japanese cities and savage Japanese rearguard actions delayed a conclusion to the war. Nevertheless there was a feeling that the end of the World War was nigh. Peace, holidays, rebuilding and the new Government were the main things on the home agenda.

The task of firing the old K class locomotive as it hauled the lightweight train from station to station en route to York, and halted for its numerous small tasks, was no weighty duty for Joe. He was pleased to have escaped from the job of cleaning and now to be acquiring another firing shift. His target was the acquisition of his second year of firing shifts and a new level of pay. Three hundred and twenty firing shifts to equate to one year's experience took a lot of obtaining.

"I was forty years of age when I got my first year's firing in," said Bob, the cheerful and talkative York driver. "Thirty years old when I became a passed cleaner. You young buck's today don't know how lucky you are, firing and even driving at such young ages." He was repeating the old refrain of the prewar railwayman, "That's what the war's done for you."

"It's an ill wind that blow's no one any good," returned Joe but let the conversation between them turn to the magic of the past, and how things used to be.

"When men were men and women were double breasted," joked Bob.

"I thought it were 'Wooden engines and iron men'," returned Joe with the same light-hearted humour that often dominated relationships between two men on a locomotive footplate.

"That was before they discovered women. Go and see how Ron's coping when we stop at Sander. In fact look at him every time we stop."

"Do we need to bother Bob? He's only a locomotive fireman. There's plenty more where he came from. Me for instance." Joe continued the joking vein as they drew into Sander. Then, as an afterthought told him that his joke sounded crude and uncaring, he added, "You know what I mean Bob. That's how the gaffer's think on us."

"Coal for the fire. Grist for the mill. That's what we all are in this life. Expendable," he grinned at Joe, then nodded in the direction of the train, "Go and see Ron."

The small quantity of traffic was soon transferred from platform to train and vice versa. Joe looked in on the sleeping Ron and climbed back onto his footplate as Bob put steam into the engine's cylinders. "He's alright Bob, sleeping, well he looked like he was asleep but he opened one eye when he heard me."

"Like him. Sleep anywhere, he can. Better than him writhing about in pain." He looked back along the platform as they slowly urged the train on the road towards the next station and York. "You were saying," continued Bob as Joe straightened from his firing task, "He's only a locomotive fireman."

"Yes," responded Joe wondering what he'd started, with his off the lip remark.

"Have you ever heard that piece of poetry. It's called 'Only a Locomotive Fireman'. It's long, but I remember it all. With Joe standing close by and with his own eye on the track Bob started his recitation to the rhythm of the wheels on the rails.

"Only a Locomotive Fireman, with a pick and shovel in hand,
Making the steam to move millions around the land;
Through tunnels, o'er bridges, through blinding snow and rain,
But only a locomotive fireman, the man on every train.
Only a locomotive fireman with a pick and shovel in hand,
But he keeps the trains a' going, all over this land."

Bob paused while he blew his engine whistle to warn working platelayers on the line. He turned to Joe and picked up the rhythm of the wheels once again and continued loudly into Joe's ear.

"Over the hills and through the valleys, in sunshine, and hail,
He keeps the steam pressure up boys, while a'flying the rail.
Only a Locomotive Fireman, but for weary hours he's fired,
Old Scrap Heap, up and down the line till every bone's tired;
Then he lays down his shovel, but no rest for him, poor man.
Then he goes, beneath 'Old Scrap', to clean her full ash-pan."

Bob paused again to sound his whistle for the signals at Ganton
and then continued;

"Firing Old Scrap Heap for his victuals and his clothes;
Little pleasure with his family, and little time to sleep,
Only a Locomotive Fireman, firing old Scrap Heap
Only a Locomotive Fireman, with his eye on the hill,
Only a Locomotive Fireman, but steadily on he goes
But train times and train safety depend on his skill."

"That was good Bob. Where did you get it?"
"It's just one of those poems that goes the rounds."
Joe knew what he meant, there were lots of footplate poets about,
songsters too. He wondered why? He'd heard Jim Simpson say that it
was the rhythm of the wheels and the engines that put poetry and song
into footplatemen's blood.

He'd been with Jim Simpson screaming down through Sandsend
Tunnel and he'd heard him reciting a poem of his own about the
mesmeric little circle of light at the distant end of the mile long tunnel
as they rushed downhill towards it at the head of a train. From a speck,
to a twinkle, to a dot, then to a hole in the blackness and on to a silver
tanner, and growing to a sun and an enveloping blaze of light. Like an
all encompassing halo through which they dashed from the black of
the tunnel into the brilliance of the day.

Bob had been started. He provided Joe with an accompaniment
of short verses about railway life and humour. While they waited for
the signal at Weaverthorpe he demanded Joe's attention for his gem
which he said would appear on his headstone.

"My engine now is cold and still
No water does my boiler fill
My coal affords its flame no more
My days of usefulness are o'er

My wheels deny their noted speed
No more my guiding hands they heed
My whistle too has lost its tone
Its shrill and thrilling sounds are gone
My valves are now thrown open wide
My flanges now no need to guide
My clacks also, though once so strong
Refuse to aid the busy throng
No more I feel each urging breath
My steam is now condensed in death
Life's railway is o'er, Each station's past,
In death I'm stopped and rest at last.
Farewell dear friends and cease to weep,
In Christ I'm safe. In him I sleep."

That's a verse that you'll find on a grave stone in a cemetery near Birmingham. The driver whose grave stone it's on was killed when his boiler blew up. O'er hundred years ago. There's lots a poetry and songs from railwaymen."

"Good. I like a bit o' poetry but I'll have to look at the fire," said Joe turning away.

★ ★ ★ ★

2
Atomic happenings.

Bob braked the train for the stop at Heslerton and reminded Joe to visit the first compartment. Two crates of young white leghorn pullets and a couple of market day visitors for Malton were all that awaited them. Laura the 'War Acting Signal Woman' at the signal cabin window waved acknowledgement to the train and the crew. This was to be her last week in her railway role, the approaching peacetime economy was preparing to receive her as a student of secretarial studies. Joe waved to her and shouted, "Good luck, with your typewriter course," then left his engine cab for his visit to Ron.

A khaki-clad young soldier with a full kit bag at the level crossing pedestrian gates called, "Wait for me," then hurried across the level crossing to the engine. "What time you get into York, Jack?" he called to the driver, "I want to know whether to get off at Malton and catch the York Express or stick with you through to York?"

"Stick with us through to York. We'll be there thirty minutes before him," answered Bob. At that moment two squawking white leghorn hens fluttered in panic along the platform pursued by the overweight station porter. The birds were the better equipped for the chase, they were free and they weren't going to return to the crate.

"I was picking the crate up when the trap door opened, on its own," the porter offered defensively. "Only two got out. They'll mebbe find their way home. They were from Adams' place," he finished hopefully.

"Any news in't paper Jack?" Bob asked with a gesture in the direction of the soldier's folded paper.

"I'll say. Look at this," the soldier replied. He grounded his kit bag and displayed the 'Daily Herald' newspaper headline, 'Thousands killed in Japanese City', 'Atomic Bomb dropped on Hiroshima'.

"Atomic bomb!" exclaimed Joe, "Isn't that something to do with Einstein?"

"Course not, he's a sculptor. Or was he the film director?" Bob asked first with confidence and then latterly with doubt.

"What's Hiroshima?" asked the porter glad to encourage the distraction from the poultry episode.

"Atomic bomb! that's summat new. Is it our bomb?" Joe had read about a scientist called Einstein claiming that a new bomb could be made. But he didn't know any more.

"20,000 tons of T.N.T. That's what it says here," said the soldier who had a Royal Army Medical Corps flash on his shoulder. "That's a lot of explosive. Think what a ton of T.N.T. can do and multiply that by twenty thousand." He paused, "It's a new bomb. With a new type of explosion. From the atom."

"Democritus talked about the atom," added Joe knowledgeably.

"Who's he?" asked Bob with a grimace. "A driver at Castlebrough shed?"

"No he wa' a Greek?"

"That were Aristotle. He was a Greek." returned Bob in jest.

Joe got on his high horse and impatiently offered the gem that Democritus was an ancient Greek. "Who was the Father of atomic theory. He said that all matter comprised little building blocks which he called atoms that had the power to stick together."

"Only matter that I know about is that yeller stuff that comes out of boils like yours," contributed Bob intent on humouring his more serious companions and avoiding a more informed debate.

A feminine voice unexpectedly broke into the all-male conversation. "Atomic and molecular theory that's what you're talking about." The four men turned in the direction of Laura who had approached them unnoticed. "Einstein explained about the immense energy that is locked up in every atom of matter. Scientists have found a way of splitting the atom and causing an explosion. That's what they've done at Hiroshima in Japan." With that, and leaving her listeners 'gob struck', she reached for the 'Herald' newspaper but her next contribution was lost in the rush of escaping steam from the boiler safety valves. Joe had to climb into the cab and subdue the roar by injecting cold water into the boiler. He rejoined the group on the platform at a point where the soldier was displaying his knowledge about the new phenomenon that had joined the already awesome range of weapons with which the World War was being fought.

"Have you looked at Ron?" asked the York driver then added. "Never mind. I'll go."

Joe was glad Bob was going because he would be left to participate in the vigorous discussion about the atomic bomb and talk privately to Laura who had become one of his many railway friends that populated the lines of Yorkshire. He would always remember how Laura had handled that emergency and derailment at Heslerton nearly two years ago, and how she'd controlled Bill Ankler, Tom Rittler and the station master. Joe admired her for her academic bent but felt over-awed by her confidence, her knowledge of things that were new to him and by her forthcoming status as a student, A 'full-time' student at that, it must take some guts to go to technical college. Joe felt conscious of his own lack of achievement, he hadn't read many books, never sat the scholarship exam at eleven. Did it matter? He was going to be a locomotive driver, but 'Only a Locomotive Driver'.

The station master and the train guard ended his introspection with, "Come on you two. You've been here too long." Bob popped his engine whistle and opened his steam regulator. The gush of steam at the cylinder cocks panicked the two white leghorn pullets in the bushes at the edge of the platform and the station porter hopefully restarted his pursuit.

At the next station, when Joe went to visit the prostrate Ron, he found the soldier seated quietly opposite. He joined his loco and said, "It's better now that Ron has got company, Bob." At Malton Station Joe used the opportunity to visit the station bookstall and purchase a newspaper. He wanted to know more about the bombing at Hiroshima. Had they really dropped a hugely explosive bomb on a city of thousands of people? Yes, they probably had, civilians were legitimate targets in this greatest war of all wars.

"Do you mind if I photograph your locomotive?" a voice asked him as he walked back to his K3. To look at the man who had spoken, Joe had to take his head from his paper. The man in a floppy trilby and jodhpur type trousers could be described as casually dressed, as if on a camping holiday and prepared to rough-it a bit.

"I should think so, mate, better ask my driver, he's in charge." Joe added the latter qualification as an after thought. He was learning to be discreet about what permissions he granted to strangers. "What do you want to photograph an engine for?" Joe couldn't imagine in his wildest dreams why anyone should want to photograph a dirty, black old London and North Eastern Railway K class locomotive, 'On a bits and pieces ramshackle old parcel train too'.

"I'm interested," came the reply. He paused as if wondering whether to elaborate further, then he decided, "I'm a railway historian, I'm building up a photographic archive of L.N.E.R. rolling stock."

"Photographic archive! What's that?" His inquisitiveness was sharpened. "Sounds important. You'd better come and talk to the driver. If his engine's goin' to be in a photographic archive he'd better know. We've only got two minutes before we have to be off."

"You'll be here about ten minutes," replied the newcomer. "There's a stock train behind you and they're going to put it past you. They're popping a load of lettuce in the van for you to take through to Haxby. Look all the signals are off for the 'up main' to let him pass you."

Joe was dumbfounded. "By God! You know a lot. Are you a railwayman?"

"No."

"How d'you know all this?"

"I had a talk with the station inspector when I came on the platform. I always do when I'm poking about and photographing. I had a talk with the signalman in Malton East box too. I've been photographing that G5 tank engine in the Whitby bay-platform too."

Joe climbed aboard the footplate of his K3 and invited the photographic archive man to follow him.

"Are you train spotting?" asked Bob good humouredly.

"Sort of," returned the visitor, "I prefer to think of myself as a railway historian. I'm compiling a photographic record, a visual archive. I prefer the word visual rather than photographic record because I collect maps, posters, track plans, timetables, drawings and the like."

"Well, I don't mind being in your visual record. Put me proper name on anything you take concerning me."

"Will you get out on the platform? With your fireman too, an' I'll take your photograph. We don't have many minutes, the up line boards are off for a stock train to pass."

The photo opportunity was rushed but Joe and Bob co-operated and gave their personal details to the photographer. "I'm coming to York with you. I've got a ticket," he said, "I'll put my gear in a compartment."

"Do you get co-operation from the railway company?" asked Bob.

"Always, if I've time to ask properly. I'm becoming a recognised railway historian."

"Do you write books?" asked Joe raising his voice above the sound of the passing empty train that was moving rolling-stock from Castlebrough to another place where it was more urgently required.

"Yes, I've done a few about the footplate. I've travelled a few miles with engine crews."

"You'd better travel with us then. We'll be getting the flag in a minute," said Bob. "Go and get your things off the train and then take a few photographs of us on the footplate."

"I thought he was a bit strange," commented Joe to Bob. "I never could understand what train spotters bothered getting numbers for. And taking photographs. Why the hell do they want to spend money on photographing railways? I still think they're a bit queer. Wish I had a camera. Wouldn't photograph railways. People yes." Joe rambled on. "But come to think on it, he is different. He's an historian. That meks him different."

"He's comin', mind yer bloody pees and kews. Don't go and upset him. Might get a tip, yuh never knows. It's happened before." He joined them on the footplate, but now he'd removed his floppy trilby and acquired a tight woollen hat, clearly intending to look out of the cab as they travelled. 'He's obviously been on the footplate before,' reflected Joe.

They were off. Joe minded his 'pees and kews' but that didn't stop him from questioning the visitor during every break in his duties. Time was easily found for 'action shots' of Joe and Bob in various working poses; 'braking the train into a station', 'opening and closing the regulator', 'shovelling coal into the firebox', 'operating a water injector and using the slekker pipe'. At Hutton's Ambo Station they posed again in look-out positions while the photographer recorded them and the train from a place on the platform. Joe used the opportunity to visit Ron and found him in some distress and in conversation with the medical orderly.

"Our next stop is Kirkham Abbey, Castle Howard is closed," Joe said to them. "We'll not be long before we get to York."

"He needs a doctor, pal," said the soldier, "He's in a lot of pain. I'm no doctor but I've enough experience to know that he needs specialist attention."

Joe found their 'train spotting' friend to be a fascinating source of information on railways. He knew a surprising amount of knowledge about locomotives and he amazed Joe with his technical knowledge of the K3 locomotive on which they rode. He knew when it was made, the size of its driving wheels, and its cylinders and the length of piston travel. Joe learnt from him that the parcel train service between York and Castlebrough was shortly to be withdrawn, there wasn't enough income from passengers and parcels, "More money's spent on wages and on locomotive costs than comes in through the tills," he told them.

As their train negotiated the winding curves through the wooded countryside and Castle Howard Station, the 'train spotter' fed Joe with details of the history of the line. The line was built in 1845 and it had been planned to avoid the curving route that accompanied the River Derwent. The plan had been to drive a tunnel through the nearby Howardian Hills, it would have shortened the route by about two miles but the cost was too great. "If that plan had succeeded," the train spotter informed them, "we would never have had this opportunity of travelling by train through this beautiful country and past the ruins of Kirkham Abbey." He took pictures of each station as they passed. "I'm doing this line today because they are cutting this train out and I want to write an article about it."

"You a writer as well. That's interesting, I've never met anybody that writes for publication." Joe carried on to recall his first firing shift on this line with old Bob Laker. 'Old Bob who'd died suddenly at work just recently,' Joe recalled his memory of the event and amused 'train spotter' by recounting how he'd thrown his shovel into the firebox at Kirkham Abbey during the raid and the blackout. "That night I nearly handed in my notice and joined the army," he laughed. "Don't put that in your book will you? I never told nobody what happened to the shovel not even old Bob."

"Jack!" exclaimed a voice outside the cab as they drew up alongside Kirkham Abbey platform. "Jack." There was urgency in the voice. Bob turned and looked out from the cab onto the uplifted face of the medical orderly. Bob wasn't surprised to be addressed as Jack; it was a common Yorkshire habit to address strangers by the name of Jack. "Your friend on the train is bad, too bad, I think he needs a doctor."

Bob was off the train quickly for a man of his bulky stature. "Ron. How are you?" He showed concern, at the sight of Ron writhing and retching.

"Pain, Bob. Sharp pain."

"I'll get a doctor," replied Bob. "You look after him," he said to the soldier. "I'll get a doctor somehow." He shouted, "Joe," then turned. Joe was still on the footplate, not behind him as was expected. Joe heard the call and together with their footplate traveller arrived to view Ron.

"He is ill," offered their traveller. "May I take a look? I'm in medicine." He invited himself into the compartment and eased Ron onto his back on the upholstered bench seat and undid his overall jacket to facilitate a pressure examination of his abdomen. "I'm a G.P., a Panel Doctor as we are more often called."

"Can you give him something, Doctor?" asked Bob.

"Not any medicine. I'm on holiday. Advice is the only thing I can give him. He needs attention urgently. I think he's got appendicitis, he needs to go to hospital."

When suitably instructed by Bob, Joe ran to find the station master and then visit the signal cabin. He carried an urgent message. "Give us a path to Haxby as quick as you can," he demanded of the signalman. "We've got a sick man on board. We're not stopping at the next three stations." He didn't heed the signalman's attempts to break into the conversation. "We've nowt for Barton, Flaxton, or Strensall. Just lettuces for Haxby. Ask York Control to have an ambulance at Haxby. Appendicitis, we think. It's urgent."

The train guard had ascertained that there were only two passengers on the train and they were travelling through to York. "Let's hope there's no passengers to pick up at the other stations," commented the guard. There weren't. They sped on through the next three stations with all signals at clear. The train spotter doctor chose to travel on the footplate and his absence from the compartment worried Ron but the reason for the doctor's absence was that he didn't think the emergency justified him missing the ride on the K3.

Bob was fired by the urgency of the situation, he made the engine and train rock and roll while it travelled like an express, he kept a sharp eye on the track and blew the engine whistle at every gatehouse and cabin. Figures waved him on, the telephone call down the line had created the attention and urgency he required. One eye was always cast backwards at Ron's compartment in case the soldier waved.

With a screaming blast on the whistle, they entered Haxby Station greeted by an ambulance waiting on the road close to the level crossing gates. Ron was carefully transferred and the ambulance left with its bell ringing and adding a note of urgency. On Bob's suggestion the doctor returned to his role of passenger in a compartment. Bob said, "Better not drive into York station with you on board in case questions are asked."

The doctor agreed, "See you at York anyway. I've been fortunate to have your company." He joined them at York on number sixteen platform at the end of the journey and recorded their addresses and made a promise to post to them copies of his photographs of themselves and their engine. "When I've developed and printed them."

Joe just had to pursue the remarkable revelation that he developed and printed his own photographs. Joe had no knowledge of photography and had no idea that photographs could be produced at home on the kitchen table. They waved goodbye with pleasure, partly because in their pockets were two ten-shilling notes. "Buy yourselves a pint," he'd said.

"We'll have to take this old scrap heap to Leeman Road shed before you go for a train," said Bob to Joe. "If Ron had been with me we would have had to stable her, and another one too, to make our day up. We aren't due to book off 'til one-thirty. We'd have had to shunt the coal-cracker too."

"I'm alright, I don't care what time I get home." Joe was cheerful but still harboured thoughts about Rusty Iron's alleged threat.

The shed yard at York was immense by comparison with Castlebrough shed yard. Joe believed there were four big sheds clustered together, each with a turntable at the centre.

"Roundhouses. That's what these sheds are called," Bob informed him. "Not like yours at Castlebrough. You've got an eight-laned straight shed."

They left their empty train for the station pilot engine to draw clear and made off tender first, in the the bright sunlight, in the direction of Leeman Road. The forest of semaphore signals dipped or raised their arms at the command of unseen hands in the numerous signal boxes. A crop of knee-high ground signals, wires and rods, occupied the spaces between the rails. Joe pondered again on how it was possible to know all the signals and rails. But now he knew how, he knew the answer because he was already master of some paths through York, paths he followed with the coal train, for instance, and with the Leeds expresses. He could drive down those paths, he knew the signals he needed, and the points, and the speed restrictions. He hoped that it would be only a short time before a driver said, 'Come on. Have a go. You've got to learn sometime.' He learnt other paths and built up his own knowledge of York's expansive railway system for the day when he would be asked to 'have a go and do a bit of driving'.

"I'm not in a rush to get home," said Joe. He wasn't. The thought of being in the same town as Rusty Iron reinforced Joe's desire not to rush home. "I'm not in a rush to get home 'cause I've got a bruiser looking for me." He confessed the details to his driver as they clanked noisily backwards in the direction of York shed. "I think I'll have a walk around York for a while."

"There's a captured V2 rocket on display you ought to look at. A Spitfire too. Go and have a look at that," advised Bob. "They're in Leeman Road Gardens."

"It'd be nice to have an hour in York, on a day like this, blazing sun, the beaches will be crowded."

"The river bank will be too, that's where I like to be on a day like this, on the banks of the Ouse. You wouldn't think there was a war on would you son?"

"Hiroshima too," Joe added. "How terrible to think of all those people perishing. Wonder if it was a day like this."

"They asked for it too, they did. They started the war. They deserve to be bombed. Like that friend of yours, they were looking for a fight."

Joe ignored the final point that produced a little worry in his stomach. "This paper thinks there will be 100,000 people killed," he replied. "That's an awful lot, men, women and children. It says we will have to search our consciences. 'A new awesome power has come into our arsenals. We will have to take great care that it is never used again. The destruction of life on earth has become a real possibility,' it says."

"They can say too much in them papers. No use belly-aching. They started the war." There was a note of impatience in Bob's response so Joe did not pursue his thoughts further. He obeyed Bob's instructions to, "Set the points for that middle road between that WD engine and that Garret loco. I aren't going to do any work at the engine. I haven't got a fireman. You've got to go home. You've to see Rusty Iron." Joe was beginning to wish that he'd never mentioned his worry.

They secured their K3 on the inspection pit and made there way towards the running-foreman's office where they were greeted with, "Bob, just the willing lad I want. Can you turn 'round another two for the road? I'm in a fix. We're short of men or I wouldn't ask."

"I'm sorry Jake, I can't. I haven't got a fireman."

Jake thumbed through his daily roster. "You've got Ron Templeman. You've just come in off Castlebrough parcels."

"Ron is in hospital. He was picked up at Haxby by an ambulance."

"Go on, Bob, Tell me." He listened to Bob's account. "I'll ring the York General," he said. His questions and answers on the phone told Bob and Joe enough. Ron was in hospital. Going to have an operation for appendicitis. His wife was with him in hospital. He was going to be alright. Should have been in hospital earlier. "That's that Bob, he's going to be alright and you've got a fireman."

"Jake, be reasonable with the lad he's got to get back to Castlebrough."

"What time have you to be back at Castlebrough, son?"

"Anytime, as long as I get paid."

"You'll get paid handsomely if you finish Ron Templeman's shift and then get that Garret ready for the road, and prepare that WD engine in number five road. You could do that, couldn't you?" The foreman was asking Joe for a commitment.

"Course I could. I'd like to. I've never been on a Garret before," added Joe enthusiastically.

"That's three-and-half-hours' work for you at time-and-a-quarter pay. Only one thing, they're all wanted for half-past one. And of course there's the other jobs, the usual jobs, the 'coal-cracker' to shunt and Harrogate engine to get ready."

"Hey! Wait on a bit, what yuh arranging with him? I'm the driver. He's only the locomotive fireman."

"Only the Locomotive Fireman," chipped in Joe, "with his eye on the till. But train times and train safety depend on his skill. Remember what you told me Bob," Joe laughed with his reply.

Bob had lost the battle, he couldn't insist on not doing the extra work when Joe was so keen and there was a shortage of men. Even though the war was almost over, there was still an acute shortage of everything. There was rationing of foodstuffs, sweets, clothes, and a desperate shortage of coal. A spirit of sacrifice was still called for but there were plenty of signs of restlessness even though new political leaders had been elected in a landslide general election. Strikes were being waged by some railwaymen and miners against long hours and Sunday work. Dockers were restless and there was an acute shortage of living space which led to 'squattings' in army huts and elsewhere. People were impatient for a better standard of living, for entertainment and leisure. The annual holiday, if one was granted, was only one week each year, the working week was forty-eight hours but everyone did more. Railway workers were on a six-day week, and they were asking for more time off, better holidays and better pay.

They did the work they'd been assigned, Bob oiled and examined, Joe cleaned fires, ashpans and smoke boxes, filled sandboxes and tanks, acquired the standard tools, detonators and lamps. He particularly liked taking the huge Garret locomotive up to the electric 'coal-cracker' and drawing coal onto the engine bunker from the hoppers with the press of a button. The huge goods locomotive had four steam cylinders, two at either end, but only one boiler and two tenders. It was designed to run comfortably in both directions and pull heavy train loads of iron ore.

"I'm going to the wash-house," Bob shouted up to Joe on the footplate. "Then I'm going to see the V2 and the Spitfire. Do you want to come?"

"Yes," replied Joe from the cab of the Garret, "Don't forget to give me that travel warrant Bob."

"Don't you forget to get a good wash, You look like a chimney sweep that hasn't been washed for six months. You're going back on the cushions don't forget, you might rub up to a girl's legs. What'd you think if one called yuh a 'mucky bugger'. And," he added emphasis, "when you come to the canteen keep yer mouth shut about politics. A lot of rough lads here. As soon go on strike as come to work."

He went to the wash-house with Bob and marvelled at the number of basins and running hot water. Later Bob took him to the shed canteen, another facility he hadn't seen in a loco shed. He learnt from one fireman that there was a lodging hostel for men on long journeys who would return home with a train the following day. The smallness of his home shed with its sixteen engines seemed microscopic compared with York's magnitude.

The display of the unarmed German V2 rocket attracted much interest. It had been brought as war booty from the defeated Germany. The North of England had been too far away to be bombarded with rockets so the people of Yorkshire were viewing something which had been a terror weapon in Southern England where three thousand of them had destroyed fifteen hundred lives this year. An airforce sergeant was relaying the facts to a watching and changing crowd. Joe felt a shudder as he thought of this rocket screaming from out of the sky at 2,000 miles an hour, it carried a ton of explosive and it could not be shot down. There was no defence against it. Bob was talking to him like a regular familiar mate. "This over here. This is more my cup o' tea. The Supermarine Spitfire F Mk. IX. This I know a lot about. And the Hurricane."

"It's so small Bob. Smaller than I imagined from seeing them in the sky."

"Wingspan 36 feet 10 inches. Merlin Royce engine, 1,650 horse power. Two 20-mm cannon. Weight 5,650 lb. Four machine guns and up to 1,000 lb of bombs."

"I didn't know they carried bombs" said Joe.

"I can tell you a lot about these. Just like that doctor train spotter could tell us lots of things we didn't know about our locomotive. I can tell a lot of things about aeroplanes. I was in the Air Training Corps. I was going to join the R.A.F. but the Government applied the essential works order and made me stop on the railways."

"Seeing you are at York, I'll show you the Roman Museum if you've got time. That's a passion of mine, Roman History. I attend classes in it." He drifted on talking about everything and Joe was interested. There was nothing about politics or unions in Bob, although he was a member of A.S.L.E.F. and he voted at meetings. He didn't like controversy. Joe would describe him as a pleasant man whom he felt he'd known for a long time. 'Funny how I've got to know him so quickly, after only six hours,' pondered Joe thoughtfully, 'That's the footplate for you. It brings you close together very quickly or you realise pretty soon that you don't get on well and you've got to be careful'.

After an hour in the Roman Museum Bob showed him the Railway Institute which housed the L.N.E.R.'s Railway Museum. "That's an old 'Spinner' with a seven-feet diameter wheel. Only one driving wheel, one at each side. They did spin and slip when starting away. Used nearly as much sand as coal. They were fast though. Eighty mile an hour on York to London expresses."

Joe marvelled at the clean, green, tall-chimneyed locomotive. "Not much protection in the cab, Bob. Did you drive them?"

"Before my time. I worked with old drivers who used to work them. They told me about 'em. Same with the old copper knob over there. We'll have to go. You can come and visit here anytime. There's classes and things you can attend at this Institute. I'll have to leave you and find out how Ron is. Thanks for helping Ron and me."

3
Displaced Persons.

Joe left Bob. On the way to the station he found himself trailing a party of travellers who jabbered excitedly in a tongue he'd not heard before. All were drably dressed, many of the women wore head squares, others had a range of floppy hats, only the younger women and the girls displayed uncovered heads. There was a dominant feature that Joe noticed, their complexions were pale, sallow even, almost chalky. The older ones had gnarled worn faces that had earned an outdoor look, faces that were a bit broader than was usual and had higher cheek bones, there were hints of Asiatic features. 'They must be foreigners,' thought Joe. He hurried on in front of the party and paused in the station entrance to view them and their battered suitcases. There were about fifteen; clearly they did not know where they were going but were delighted to realise that they had found the railway station. They jabbered and bustled past Joe, who recognised the German word 'dankerschon'. 'German? They must be German, German refugees maybe' he thought. But other words were very strange. He hovered around, trying to be nosey without appearing so. A uniformed railway official was seeking someone to talk to in English.

"We're lost." Joe heard the words spoken in a London cockney dialect by a small woman. "We got on a train at Hull for Castlebrough in York, but we are at York but not Castlebrough."

The uniformed railwayman removed his peaked cap, apparently to scratch his head. "This is York but Castlebrough is a long way."

"No Castlebrough York! Look at these instructions."

"Castlebrough Yorks." He emphasised 'Yorks'. "That's Yorkshire. See it's got an 'ess' after York. They've put you on the wrong train at Hull."

A few words in German from the cockney woman created a babble of agitated protest, the ripple spread through the shuffling group. Cases flopped down, some of the group flopped on the cases. Anxiety was apparent. A torrent of incomprehensible questions, protests and pleadings washed over the station inspector. The older people amongst them displayed anxiety, Joe had moved in amongst them, more unintentionally than by design. The station public address system boomed out and a non-stop express rushed through the station. Joe found himself comforting a small boy whose tearful face occupied a space beneath a large floppy cap.

"Er ist erschrocken. Er ist Ohne Vater." Joe looked up into the broad open face of a crinkly-haired blonde who was addressing him about the small boy. A smile seemed almost to accompany her look but neither she nor the others showed any joy or enthusiasm. Joe understood broadly what she had said, he recognised the German words 'erschrocken' for frightened and 'Ohne Vater' for without Father and responded with a "Yes" but didn't volunteer any of the few words of German that he was acquiring.

The small cockney woman in charge of the party could be heard describing how she had landed at the port of Hull with the refugees from Europe but had boarded the wrong train and arrived at York. "They are immigrants, refugees, displaced persons from the war in Europe, mostly Ukrainians," he heard her saying, "They are going to work and live in Castlebrough."

"You haven't got tickets for travel to Castlebrough," the station inspector was saying.

"Course we have," responded the guide.

"You haven't got the right ticket to travel from York to Castlebrough. You'll have to pay excess fares." The inspector's ruling brought forth from her a burst of wrath, he only calmed her with promises to see what could be done. He said that he knew they hadn't intended to travel off their route. Like the 'Pied Piper of Hamlin' he blew on his flute, only his flute was a railway mouth-whistle and the throng obediently responded to his wave and followed him through the ticket barrier.

Joe decided that he really should be on his way back to Castlebrough so he muttered 'goodbye' in German. "Wiedersehen" he said softly to the boy and the blonde girl and slipped away to involve himself in his own concerns. The next train was about an hour away so he purchased a meat pie in the staff canteen and sat reading the 'good news' from the war with Japan. 'Stunning news' he suggested to himself as he absorbed the detail and the speculation about the Hiroshima event. 'Terrible news really.' He kept re-assessing it. 'Yes. terrible news for the expected 100,000 Japanese victims, men, women, children, yes children, babies, and railway workers. But I agree with it being dropped. We've got to end the war somehow. They started it, and they're fascists, just another type of Nazi.' He felt uncomfortable about the position he'd adopted but then it was war.

The three-thirty to Castlebrough was due to leave number nine platform soon. The platform was packed with hopefuls determined to get on the train when it arrived from Leeds. Joe decided to jump the queue and be first to join the train so he joined from the traffic side and passed through the guards van. He occupied a 'smoking' seat while the departing passengers still struggled to exit onto the platform against the incoming hopefuls. He wasn't surprised to see Ukrainian refugees in the corridor spilling in to occupy the seats in his compartment but he was rather surprised to be joined by the tearful boy under the large floppy cap. The lad had picked him out as offering security in the strange new land. Joe didn't discourage him, just looked into his doleful brown eyes and offered him a comforting wink of assurance. The blonde Ukrainian girl, who had earlier addressed him with a few words of German occupied the seat at the other side of 'doleful brown eyes', who in turn expressed a feeling of increased security. A muscular thirty-ish dour faced man squeezed in close to Joe, who was becoming more conscious of his own dirty state of dress. 'Good job I'm not next to a woman', thought Joe recalling Bob's advice about taking care not to rub up against some young lady's leg. 'Maybe this guy won't be keen to rub up against my mucky clothes'.

The carriage shuddered as a fresh locomotive buffered up to the train. Conversation in strange languages crisscrossed the compartment. Joe heard two men exchange the foreign sounding word "lokomotive", then they left the compartment. 'Maybe locomotive is an international word and they've gone to see the locomotive that has just backed up to the train, something we do in England. Maybe they are railwaymen, maybe locomotivemen.' Joe mused thoughtfully on but kept his seat and his silence. He wasn't scared to mix with foreigners.

The Cockney guide entered the compartment and in German checked the refugees' names against her list. Two were missing, she left and later returned with the missing men who obeyed her instruction to be seated. "Are you going to Castlebrough, young man?" She addressed Joe.

Joe's simple, "Yes," resulted in a string of questions to him about Castlebrough.

"How far? How long will it take? Can you tell us where to get off? Do you know Stone Towers Hotel on East Bank, Castlebrough? That's where we are going. These people are Ukrainian Displaced Persons from work camps in Germany."

The compartment was designed for eight people, maybe ten at the most, but there were ten occupants, not including the English guide and Joe. She would be leaving soon to supervise the rest of her party she had said. Two small adults were stretched out on coats on the two luggage racks. Suitcases and other luggage overflowed into the corridors. Cigarette smoke was making the air uncomfortable to breathe.

"They want to be all together." The guide spoke in English to Joe. "There are too many in here but they won't move." She spoke in German next in a sharper tone to all her charges. Joe didn't know what she told them but he understood the reaction from the muscular fellow who had disappeared to view the locomotive. He agitatedly pointed at Joe. His arms moved wildly as he spoke, betraying his passion, he appeared to gabble and express some anger towards Joe who heard the words 'lokomotive feuerman'. He remained passive although he sensed that the man had asked for him to leave. The cockney lady replied equally passionately and then spoke to Joe. "Please don't react. They are frightened to be in a foreign country."

"He didn't seem very frightened to me. I thought he was coming at me," replied Joe with a hint of intended humour to conceal his concern.

"No. Don't misunderstand their excited expressions. They are just as forceful when they speak to each other."

"What did he want anyway. I heard him say 'Locomotive fireman'."

"His friend said that he thought you were a locomotive fireman. They both think you should go on the engine and make more room in here."

"I will. It's crowded and smoky in here."

"No please don't go. I would like you to stay. They're nice really. I can't ride with them all the way because I've got others in another compartment. If you will stop with them, please? I would like them and me to have you with us and I want to ask you many things about Castlebrough." She had to turn away from Joe to the Ukrainian man, to listen to him and reply. "He thinks you are maybe the fireman on this train's engine."

"I'm not, I'm a passenger going home. I can find somewhere else."

"Please don't go. That man was a fireman on the Ukrainian railways before the German invasion. He's just interested in railways. When we are all settled I'll come back and talk with you."

Joe could hear the engine's large vacuum ejector exhausting from the chimney top, the brakes were easing from the wheels as vacuum was created in the trainpipe. His watch displayed the time to be almost three-thirty and time to depart. Black smoke drifted down from the engine and past the windows raising an unspoken criticism of the fireman in Joe's mind, 'Why is he firing it in the station, that's bad practice. He should have built up his fire and burnt the smoke before he arrived in to the station'. The guard's whistle sounded, the engine whistle replied and the regulator opened. The engine coughed at the chimney top. The two Ukrainians who had shown interest in locomotives rose and lowered the window in the door. Their heads popped out and they viewed the signals and chattered. Joe could make out only the words that sounded like 'kleine lokomotive'. Maybe they were saying that the locomotive on the train was very small. He didn't like them, he decided. They were probably saying that the train engine was very small against Ukrainian locomotives. Joe knew that they would have big locomotives in the Soviet Union because the vastness of the territory.

The locomotive slipped, gathered its 'feet' and urged again. He had no idea what engine was on the train or how long the train was, he'd been neglectful of his usual practice of viewing the locomotive because of his unwitting involvement with the refugees. The compartment was full of incomprehensible conversation as the pulsating York station passed by their window. The crossing over the River Ouse raised further interest amongst the group.

Joe sensed that their being in another foreign country was unnerving. He warmed to them with a surge of sympathy, they were from German work camps. He shuddered. He recalled the exposure on film and in the newspapers of Belsen, Buchenwald, Auschwitz, to name only a few of the Nazi horrors that the defeat of Germany had revealed. 'Were these people victims of that kind of horror?' he thought. The deeper he thought, the more he felt sympathy for his companions.

Slumber and quiet settled on the party as the train sped on through Haxby and beyond to a new life for the immigrants. Joe was compressed between his seated companions but he managed the occasional cigarette, and to read his paper and pay particular attention to the reports of German refugees being expelled in large numbers from the Baltic counties, Poland, Czechoslovakia and others. 'What a mess Europe's in? Will the scores ever be settled and peace ever return to these starved and destroyed lands?' He visited the toilet and then pushed his way back into his seat and unintentionally fell into a deep sleep.

"The train approaching number three platform is the four-twenty-eight from Leeds." Castlebrough station's public address system aroused him. He was surprised to have slept in the hub-hub of the smelly, hot compartment. The journey-time had gone in an instant, he wanted to be off but so did everybody else. Impatience was the order of the day. The guide was in his path on the platform, he pushed down the one step, not thinking to offer to help with the suitcases of the party.

"Mister!" The voice of the guide was unmistakable. She caught his elbow. "Mister, can you help us to find where we are going?" Joe recalled her earlier request which, he admitted to himself he had hoped would not be repeated. His personal concern about the Iron brothers which had overshadowed the day returned. Anxiety bit into his stomach. Threats were threats, they mostly did not materialise, but not so with Rusty Iron. According to the legend he enjoyed having a score to settle, especially when it was going to be settled with violence. Joe knew the local belief that when the 'iron man' made a threat he always accomplished his objective. Rusty, in his proper name of Robert Iron, was said to have served two prison terms for violence against persons, and one of them was in the feared army 'Glasshouse' at Richmond. 'How have I managed to cross a hardcase like Iron?' he asked himself.

"It's a mile to the hotel. It's too far to walk with cases," offered Joe. "You could go by taxi."

"That's what I should do, but I don't have enough money left for all these taxis. I could get some tomorrow when the banks open."

'Was she hinting that she'd like to borrow money from him?' he asked himself. Not only did he not have much money but he viewed with dismay the prospect of lending money to foreigners whom he might never see again. He had misunderstandings with Rusty Iron to settle. He didn't want to add to that a misunderstanding with these foreigners.

"What about the bus?" he asked as he was unwillingly swept through the ticket barrier by the anxious group he was in danger of adopting. The warm feeling of a small hand thrust into his hand seemed to confirm the likely adoption.

"There's fifteen of us, with cases. Could you put all of us on the right bus?" she asked.

He shuddered at the task. "You could," replied Joe. "The conductor would tell you where to get off." As they talked their shambolic group drifted in the direction of the taxi rank and the local bus stop. Joe didn't want to get involved, even though the wave of sympathy that he'd experienced earlier for these victims of Hitler started to trouble him.

"That's what we'll have to do. Can you show us the bus?"

"The 101 United bus. Or the 100. Red double deckers from there." He pointed. "Cost you about three-ha'pence each."

She shouted instructions in German to her charges. "I'll have to check them all on," she told Joe.

Joe waved the bus to a halt and helped move the luggage. The conductor who had been ready to offer help suddenly showed concern. "Can't get them all in here. Half of you will have to take a later bus."

"What am I going to do? I can't split them. Can you go with these Mister?" she asked Joe. "I'll get the others on the next bus." The warm hand of the tiny figure pulled Joe onto the step of the bus. Fate had decreed that he was going to be good Samaritan.

"Catch the next bus to St James's Church, don't get on the wrong one. 100 or 101, I'll be waiting for you when you get off," Joe explained as he boarded the bus at the end of his charges.

He waited, still accompanied by the small boy and the blonde who repeatedly spoke to the boy. He joined them on the climb up the hill to the Stone Towers Hotel which had just been de-requisitioned by the army. It was spartan and showed the marks of army occupation, but it had the feel of home to these travellers from grimmer living spaces. He took his leave, the boy with the doleful eyes hung grimly to his hand which had offered such simple solace, he nodded his regards to the blonde and the others and departed amid the gratitude of echoing Danke schons.

★ ★ ★ ★

Joe could not avoid being in town two days later on the next Saturday evening. Dan West was home from the Leatherhead Emergency Services Hospital and a night out on the town was planned. The light, warm nights and the thousands of holiday makers in town created a friendly atmosphere, but trouble-makers were in town. There were always trouble-makers on Saturday nights when money and drink flowed more freely than at other times.

Joe's only concern was with the possibility that Rusty Iron might be packing his six-shooters and looking for a show-down at 'O.K. Corral'. That was Dan's amusing forecast of what might happen. "I'll be sailing in with you Joe. Just get 'em to me chair and I'll hit them," he confirmed as his hand-propelled chair negotiated the narrow oak-lined entrance of the old town public house.

Frank Sutton and Alf South were waiting for Joe and Dan and they were in conversation with Ron, a disabled local lad who exhibited pronounced movement difficulties and grossly impaired speech. Sadly his disabilities had earned him the title of, 'spastic Ron'. His home-made waist-high wooden box on four old pram wheels was his walking aid, it also carried his belongings including his money in full view on a small tray.

"Drink - Dan?" Ron questioned, as Dan's wheelchair turned to face the table alongside him.

"Thanks Ron. Half o' pint o' mild."

Alf fetched the drinks and helped himself to Ron's coins. "You a'right Ron?" he asked as he took Ron's rubber drinking tube from the money tray and placed it in the glass of beer for Ron.

"Yeh! You've had yer op. aint you Dan?" asked Alf. An exchange of news up-dated the friends on Dan West's fortunes in the E.M.S. hospital and the promise of a training place in Exeter's St Loyes' Training College for the Disabled.

"A watchmaker. That sounds good. Should be good money," Joe commented as they all discussed the result of Dan's letter to the Queen.

"What - about - me?" Ron jerked into the conversation with his face twisting and grimacing with difficulty. "Would they-take me, to be a - watch - maker, Dan?" They all laughed at the vision of Ron's threshing arms making fine adjustments to a watch. Ron enjoyed the laugh at his expense, he enjoyed it more because he'd engineered it. Joe placed a pint of beer on Ron's money tray and inserted the drinking tube.

"Rusty!" Ron got the word out and directed attention to Rusty Iron's entry into the room. "And, Scrap."

Joe experienced a shudder at the sight of the big bull-necked, red haired Rusty Iron and his young brother, Scrap entering the bar-room. They heard the call from Ron and indicated their intention to join him when they'd obtained drinks. Joe felt cornered. He shuddered more obviously as Rusty and Scrap joined them at the table. He felt his shudder threaten to evolve into a definite shake as Rusty said in Joe's direction, "I've been wanting to see you," but instead of pursuing Joe he fell into easy conversation with Ron, it seemed easy because they talked more casually between themselves than Ron could talk with others.

"Do you know Rusty?" Joe asked of Ron when he had an opportunity.

"Yes. He's - me - cousin," Ron replied.

Joe suddenly waved an acknowledgement in the direction of two figures who peered through the bar-room door. "The Ukrainian locomen," said Joe to Dan and Frank. He waved them over, not that he wanted to welcome them, he felt that their presence somehow or other altered the balance of forces. "Friends," he said in English as he waved his hand around the company. "Drink?" he asked and illustrated the art of drinking out of an imaginary glass to reinforce his question. They declined, maybe because they had no language to share with the company. They indicated that they were going to make towards the exit.

Rusty noted Joe's conversation with the fleeting visitors. "Locomen, that's it. You're Boxer Wade aren't you?" He shouted across the table. "Just reminded me, that did, why I wanted to see you." He broke the flow of his thought. "Who you think yuh pushin' about?" he asked Alf South who was squeezing past with his hands full of glasses.

"I'm pushin' you. Get out of the way," said the comparatively small Alf South looking up threateningly into the big face. "Want to make something of it?"

"No, do you? But I'll put your face in that ice box in a minute. Where's that southpaw. I want to see him." Joe was vanishing through a toilet doorway when Rusty set his eyes on him. "You'd think he don't want to see me."

"He does, Rusty," informed Frank Sutton mischievously. "He was just saying that he hoped he'd see you tonight. Summat on his mind."

"I've summat on my mind. I think southpaw's got the answer." He laughed, emptied his glass and pushed his way to the gent's toilet just as Joe emerged.

"What's he mean calling him southpaw?" asked Alf.

"It's a boxing name for a boxer who leads with his right. That's what Joe did. He led with his right," answered Frank.

"Rusty's got him. He's got him up against the wall," said Alf. "Is he going to kiss him?"

"Or batter him," said Frank without any concern.

"Rusty's red stubbled chin was close enough to Joe's face for him to feel the presence of Rusty's breath. "Come over here, southpaw. Near our Ron. I've summat to ask yuh?"

"Joe's stomach was tight, knotted and churning all at once. He said nothing because he didn't want to hear is own shaky voice. He obliged by sitting near Ron. He afterwards remembered thinking 'He won't hit me so close to his disabled cousin Ron. I'll shelter near Ron'.

Rusty joined the conversation. "Locomen I heard you say about them two? That's what I wanted to ask you about Joe. Ron told me you were a locoman. Didn't yuh Ron? I wanted to ask you about that."

Joe had just received a stunning upper-cut. His mind was blank. He didn't show his fear or his relief. He waited for Rusty to imbibe a long draft from a newly filled glass.

"I'm a ship's stoker," Rusty continued to dominate the talking. "I'd like to do a spell on the land. Like to get a job on the footplate. Ron sez yuh'd know what I ought to do. Your pal's Dad is somebody down at the shed, he sez."

Joe told him. In great detail he told him and with enthusiasm. He told him about the day he'd just had, "Boring and uneventful? Not really! "Come down to the shed tomorrow if you want, I'll show you a few engines. And tell yuh how to apply. Good idea to find out, things aren't always what yuh think they're going to be." As he made that remark he recalled his own feelings about Rusty and what Frank had led him to expect.

"He's okay Joe, isn't he?" said Frank. "There's a whole family like him at home. There's Wrought Iron, Cast Iron, Scrap of course. Flat Iron his dumpy sister and Sheet Iron." Frank was grinning and Joe knew why.

1
Not Tyred Enough.

"Who was that girl I saw you with last night?"

"She's a displaced person from the Ukraine," replied Joe to Johnny Marsay.

"What's one of them? She's a bit older and bigger than you ain't she? Reckon you'd have a job to displace her."

"Displaced persons are people who have been displaced by the war. Thought you'd know that. Refugees, if you like," Joe added importantly. He'd finished getting his engine ready for the road and had time to talk. "She was captured by the Germans in the Ukraine when they invaded. She and her Mother were shipped off with a lot of others to be forced workers in Germany."

As Jim Simpson oiled the right-hand outside big-end on D49 locomotive 2758 named 'Cattistock', standing on number two inspection pit at Castlebrough shed, he offered his contribution to the conversation. "There are about 13 million people in Europe who have been displaced by the war. Just look at what's happening to the Germans who lived in Poland, Czechoslovakia and the Baltic countries. They lost the war after attacking other countries, now they're being kicked out without any sympathy."

"Was that woman you were with, one of them?" asked Frank who was idly leaning on a shovel with it's blade embedded in a pile of clinker and ashes, "Are yuh going out with her?"

"Sort of. We don't go dancing. Just pictures and walking."

"A bit tame in it?"

"Not really, she's had an interesting life. She was forced with her mother to go to Germany and work in one of Hitler's work camps." He paused, "I should say she's had an eventful life." He continued, "I shouldn't think life in a concentration camp was interesting, more like bloody awful."

"She talks English does she?" queried Frank.

"Not much. She talks German, and Ukrainian. I think she talks another language to Anna Vladimirovna. Someone sez she talks Russian," answered Joe. He felt a sense of achievement after managing to pronounce Anna Vladimirovna with confidence.

Jim Simpson, listening while he oiled the locomotive they were going to use on the 3.25 to York, added, "Poland is next door to Ukraine. She would know Polish."

"You can't have much to talk about if she can't talk English. How d'you manage?"

"She's learning English and I'm learning German."

"Can she tell you that she loves yuh?" asked Jim with a wide grin.

"Yes," responded Joe treating the question as of scholarly interest in German but determined to also play the fool with them. "Ich leibedich. 'and' Mein Leibling. Wasser und donner und blitzen. Du bist ein dumpfkopf Englisch schweinhund. Yo ist dein brains?"

"That sounds impressive," replied Frank. "What did you say?"

"I said, Yes my darling I do love you. I do think Hitler burnt down the Reichstag and blamed it on the Communists. And I don't believe Polish troops attacked Germany and started the war. How much is bread? Where is your Mother. I like to mow the fields and then roll with you in the hay."

"All that?" asked Frank with amazement. "In just those few words. But you weren't really saying those things to her were you? Do you sit on a park bench and talk about bread and burning down the Reichstag?"

"We talk about anything because I want to learn German and she wants to learn English."

"Funny way to spend an evening with a girl. What do yuh call her? Do you like her?"

"Course I do. Her name's Katiya. Sometimes I have to spend the evening in their room in the Stone Tower Hotel. Her Ma won't let her go out with me, She's a little screwed up woman, only half the size of Katiya. But she doesn't half bash her about the room and scream at her. Her Mam wants her to stop goin' out with 'Inglish man and marry Ukrainish man'. When I go into their room there's hell on. Her Ma throws things at her and me, and screams, and thumps Katiya. Then she cools down a bit and gets into bed after sayin' I can stop with Katiya. When I leave to go home she shouts, 'Watch out for the Yids. The Yids'll get yuh.' She cackles, she's a right old crone. 'Hitler's a fine man,' she shouted once. I can't understand her much. She can't speak many words of English or German."

"Funny she should think Hitler a good man. He invaded the Ukraine and killed millions," said Frank.

"Katiya says Hitler took them to Germany and gave them work, food and safety." Joe sought to explain, "They say Russians are bad. Katiya said they were told 'Stalin bad and Hitler good.' Funny that they believed it."

"It's funny what you can be made to believe with a gun stuck up your hooter," added Jim Simpson and the listeners all "ayed" or grunted a form of approval.

As driver Simpson and fireman Wade backed their locomotive slowly under the darkening sky in the direction of Castlebrough station they talked more about Joe's displaced-person friends. Rain was promised but it would mean no extra hardship for the two men on the footplate of the D49 Shire class loco which would make easy work of the eight-coach corridor express to York.

They attached their locomotive and prepared for the departure. Joe's experience of foreigners and distant cultures unfolded. "There looked like there was going to be hell to play if I didn't stop seeing Katiya. Her Ma would shout at me when she saw me, 'Go away Inglish man. Katiya's going to marry Ukrainish man'. She would throw little stones at me. Katiya would run from her Ma to me. But when she got home afterwards she would be bashed by her mother."

"I thought she was a big lass and her Ma was a little scrat."

"Right! But that doesn't stop her Ma. Katiya just takes it and cowers. She'd never hit her Ma back. Would you?"

"No, but then my Mam would never bash me and tell me who I was going to marry," laughed Jim.

"Customs they say. The women have to marry whom they're told."

"How horrible."

The train guard's whistle and flag gave them instructions to leave and steam surged to the cylinders and the loco moved the train and passengers on their way. In five minutes they were away from Sander and making good speed. The engine was fast and economic but she tossed about on the rails. "She's a rough rider," shouted Jim. "Must be ready for the shops."

"She's alright Jim. I can stand up. Let's give her a run, see what she can do. I'll keep her safety valves popping. She's good engine, good steamer but bad rider. Let her go Jim, I feel like a run. They've put the speed limit up to seventy from here to Rillington."

Jim knew that information, it was his job to know. "I'll make you work for a bit, and we'll see how she rides," returned Jim with a grin.

Joe hadn't finished yet, he tried another tack. "I'll do a bit of driving for you Jim, if you like? I know the road." His head was aching, he didn't feel very well. But he considered that a sit down on the driver's seat would do him good.

"Time'll come son when you'll get over here. You just get some practice in with the shovel, I hear that you are good at making camel's humps." Joe laughed back he hadn't really expected Jim to let him drive an express train but Joe was staking his claim early. He knew he'd get a bit of driving in the shed yard first and then later be allowed to drive a shunting engine. In the meantime he was just doing what all young fireman would do, state a wish 'to have a go' until one day a driver would pass the controls over for a short time.

A pleasing fast run under the threatening sky rewarded their efforts. The engine bucked furiously on the rails and raced away to Malton. The rain fell and after the stop at Malton they pitched confidently into the next 21 miles to York along the picturesque weaving track through Castle Howard and Kirkham Abbey.

The driving rain hit the loco very hard, completely obscuring the spectacle windows and causing rain to torrent in a sheet from the cab roof. It overshot the cab side-windows and fell on the two heads that peered from the windows. The flat agricultural plain of the vale of York provided perfect terrain for the railbed. The sky was dark with heavy rain clouds, jagged lightening forked down onto the Howardian Hills as the eight-coach passenger train sped on.

"Flaxton's home board's off, Jim. Back board's off now too," Joe shouted.

"Soon be able to shut off at Haxby and coast into York, don't overdo the fire Joe," Jim shouted back across the cab as Joe commenced to fire. "We'll be stood in York for ten minutes. Don't want her blowing off."

Joe, balancing carefully on the bucking wooden floor of the cab, and firing as they sped on, was taking great care to keep his right foot clear of the restless steel flapper plate covering the gap between the engine and tender. He'd lost the soles off his boots to the sharp edge of the plate before now and didn't want it to happen again.

The D49 engine was a very restless rider, it was tossing the cab and the crew about tirelessly while it was in fast motion. Every engineman knew the reason why D49 locomotives were rough riders at speed, the engine's wheelbase comprised a four-wheeled leading bogie followed by four large coupled driving wheels, but no two-wheeled pony beneath the cab to give the engine better stability at speed.

Joe knew there wasn't much chance of his engine blowing off steam in York Station, his boiler gauge glasses showed the water level bobbing half-way down the glass, there was plenty of room for more water to stop her blowing off. He examined his firebed and added fresh coals in order to burn off the black smoke before they arrived at York Station. A full head of steam proclaimed itself on the steam pressure gauge and Simpson made use of it by opening the regulator to its fullest extent.

"What happened next with the displaced person? You didn't finish telling me," Jim shouted to Joe who returned to the subject of the Ukrainian girl.

"I'm still seeing her. It isn't easy though because of the death threat letter." The engine rolled wildly and Joe caught hold of the firescreen to steady his passage as he threatened to roll with it.

"I hadn't heard about the death threat," shouted Jim just as the engine tossed Joe across the cab. "She's a bloody rough rider." Jim caught Joe by his shoulder as he staggered.

"She's fast Jim, though." Joe raised himself alongside Jim Simpson on the driver's side of the locomotive and returned to the subject of the conversation they'd been sharing on the run up to Flaxton. "Her mother persisted with her opposition to me seeing Katiya. One morning my Dad was having breakfast and opening a letter. Suddenly he said, "What's this bloody lot? Someone wants to kill you. I gobbled a bit. Couldn't believe I was hearing right."

"This, he said chuckin' a letter on the table. It's got Josef on it. I take it that means you. It starts off 'Ukrainish man going to kil you'. I could see," shouted Joe into Jim's ear, "that someone, I think it was Katiya's Mother, had written a letter to me in a bit of German, an' English, an' Ukrainian."

"Look out that side Joe."

Joe dutifully finished his reply and skipped back across to his side of the cab and looked out at the drenched fields that were a mixture of ripe grain and stubble, fallow ground and ploughed earth. He read the signals and viewed the track ahead, he made a mental note to finish his account of his brush with the Ukrainians for Jim Simpson when they pulled into York. The loco travelling at speed was too noisy to facilitate easy conversation.

Flaxton flashed by and they raced on in the driving rain towards Strensall Station with all signals off. To warn road users not to cross the lines at the level crossing they obediently sounded their engine whistle as they passed the whistle board. Joe's head was out in the storm, looking for anyone on the line and checking that the semaphore signal boards were really in clear position. It was impossible to view the track and the signals through the spectacle windows. The loco jumped and swayed. Joe liked a rough ride at times, he hung onto the window side and listened to the rhythmic sounds of the speeding locomotive. The wheel below his seat cracked and clanked, a shudder seem to affect the engine frame.

'She does ride rough,' mused Joe. The noise below his seat rose rapidly into an alarming clanking, banging and wrenching. He looked across at Jim Simpson, they exchanged glances. An exploding sound echoed through the engine frame. Joe felt the floorboards beneath his feet move and shift him bodily upwards, a heavy shower of large sized ballast sprayed the window through which Joe looked. He leapt away in a startled panic from the impact his feet and seat received. His head spun with a blow. Simpson slammed his regulator shut and applied the train's brake instantly as Joe fell on to him. The firescreen broke away from the boiler front, the wooden cab floor jumped into the air and the damper controls reared up from the impact below. The seat on which Joe had been seated buckled upwards as the steel side of the cab folded like cardboard and the glass side windows burst into fragments.

Events happened fast; yet they stood still, frozen in time, just like a still photograph, just like the time when he'd witnessed the fatal crash between two Hull trains at Castlebrough. Joe hung onto the water injector wheel close by Jim. The brakes were on, the steam was off, the engine bucked as the driving wheel beneath the fireman's side exploded into fragments which destroyed part of the cab and threw large bits of steel tyre back alongside the train.

"Are we off, Jim?" yelled Joe as his still photograph melted into turmoil. The onward rush of the wounded loco seemed not to heed the emergency application of the brake, the rocking and rolling was violent as the broken wheel and connecting rod threshed and obeyed the anarchy of accident.

"Don't bloody know?" Jim Simpson's face displayed a definite pallor as he responded to Joe's yelled question meaning 'Are we derailed?' 'Are we off the rails?' "We're doin' seventy."

"Bloody pray, Jim. Bloody pray." responded Joe wondering why he'd said that.

"Keep away from that side," instructed Jim.

"Yuh bloody kidding," Joe had to say something. The damage to the cab seemed complete, nothing more flew about but the damaged wheel tossed the cab about with a noisy, sickening, bumping vibration.

"The brake's biting."

"She's slowing, Jim."

They flew past Strensall platform and Jim had a fleeting glance of startled figures on the down line platform witnessing the plight of the slowing express in obvious distress.

"We'll know in a bloody minute, Joe. Can you get this side injector on? She'll be blowing-off in a minute and frightening the passengers," Jim shouted but he was in control, he knew what to do. Joe put his water injector into operation without panic, he saw blood on Jim's leg but Jim didn't seem to be aware as he yelled, "She's stopping on the rails, I think."

Now time took an age, they lost speed slowly accompanied by the slowing thumping vibration, Jim eased the train brakes to avoid a sudden dramatic halt. "Joe, get up to the cabin, Rule 55. Tell him to stop traffic on both lines. I'll get some detonators and protect the facing line."

"Yuh leg Jim. It's bleeding like hell."

"Hell! Aye. I didn't know. Hurts like hell now. Your face is cut."

"I'll tek the bangers forward." Joe felt his numbed cheek and examined the blood on his hand. "Only a graze. I can run, you can't."

Jim didn't argue. Joe was right. "I'll get back to the cabin. Maybe the guard'll protect the back-end and get to the cabin."

They came to a sudden halt as the brakes bit, a halt like hitting a brick wall at slow speed but it shouldn't have caused any harm to passengers.

"Let's have look-see," said Joe with detonators and a red flag in his grasp. "Should be able to squeeze out of that side." They both left the cab by the damaged side into the driving rain.

"We've lost a tyre off the rear driving wheel," was Jim Simpson's quick response when he viewed the damage. "Hell, its broke up. Thrown chunks of steel all over. Side rod's bust. No wonder it made a hell of a racket." Jim's comments were quick, he didn't waste time. "Get running up front to stop an on-coming train if need be. Leave the crackers on the line, don't want to see passengers on the track with an express coming down to plough through them."

"The signals are all at danger, Jim, so it should be alright."

"I'm stuck Joe." Jim winced, "Can't walk far on this leg. You've got that cut on your face Joe, not bad, but wants attention."

"Look at the side of the train. Half the windows is missing in the first two carriages. Might be passengers injured, Jim."

"Yes. Get your bloody self away Joe. Get them crackers down as quick as you can. There might be lumps of tyre on the rails."

Joe raced off. The rain drenched his overalls quickly. 'September! And all this rain,' he grumbled to himself. He ran fast but didn't feel well, his head throbbed and his throat burnt. He hoped he wasn't starting with a cold. He knew it would take him a long time to run three-quarters of a mile, put his detonators down on the line and return. The protection had to be carried out even though all the signals were at danger because a train at speed in a rainstorm could miss its signals and plough into passengers on the line even if there was no dangerous debris to de-rail it.

There appeared to be a few passenger injuries caused when the sides of the first two coaches were badly damaged by flying metal and ballast. The injured passengers were few because the corridors in the two coaches were on the affected side and all the passengers had been seated in the compartments.

"What caused your leg injury Jim?" asked Joe when he found him being tended in the small waiting-shelter on Strensall Station.

Jim ignored the question and showed his concern for his locomotive. "Have you been back on the engine? Did you turn the water off?"

"Yes Jim. There's a platelayer in the cab keeping an eye on things. What's wrong with your leg?"

"A deep cut. I've got to go to hospital. You'll have to look after the loco. I'd rather stop here with you but they say I need attention."

"Stitches. That's obvious," said one of the small group with Jim in the waiting shed. "You need that cut covering young man."

"It'll wait a while yet. Get a plaster on Joe's face, Jim insisted. "We've got the engine to think off, and the train." Jim didn't fancy going off to hospital and leaving Joe. "Bind me up with those bandages, I'm going to look at the engine, I'm not badly hurt." He turned his head towards Joe, "There's my gear in the locker. and papers I've got for a Council meeting tomorrow." He wouldn't be persuaded otherwise.

"The tool vans are coming from York. They'll be about half an hour," said a member of the station staff to Jim as he straightened up. "They asked if the engine could be repaired and driven to York. I said 'No', It's bust. A wheel's come off."

"Let's look at her. Let me lean on yuh Joe. This is more gammy than I thought." He accepted a ride on a station porter's barrow down the platform to a point closer to the engine.

There was a small interested crowd of locals and railway workers around the wrecked loco. The whole of the five-feet, eight-inch diameter tyre and flange had disintegrated and been scattered over a wide area, some of it had been collected and piled near the loco. The side-rod had broken its pivot crank from the wheel, it was bent and still attached to the leading driving wheel but freed from the damaged trailing wheel, it had trailed and threshed about during the momentum of the engine after the tyre had disintegrated.

Joe climbed up the damaged cab side. Jim shouted up that he couldn't climb, "Open the steam cocks. Turn the small vacuum ejector off. Tie everything down." His interest in the state of his engine was rudely interrupted by a shout.

"Taxi! Driver! There's a taxi to take you to York General." A figure further up the line was approaching him and shouting.

"The tool vans are coming, Jim," said Joe nodding in the direction of York. "So long Jim, mebbe see you in York."

The vans hauled by an A6 class side-tank engine pulled up on the neighbouring main line. Engine fitters and their tools were soon on the ground and a locomotive inspector consulted with the fitters. Passengers had been relocated on undamaged parts of the train and the two damaged coaches were uncoupled.

"She won't move under her own steam," stated the foreman fitter.

"We could try her when we strip down the damaged parts and check everywhere. We'd get her into that siding somehow. She's not going to travel far with that busted wheel," the loco inspector answered. It proved impossible to move her under her own steam so the tool vans' engine had to inch her into the nearby siding and Joe threw the fire out of the firebox to make the engine safe to leave at Strensall. The effort exhausted him and his head pounded. A locomotive came out from York to take the passenger train forward after inspections had proved that the train and the track were in safe order. With his and Jim Simpson's personal belongings, Joe rode on the footplate of the rescuing engine back to York where he reported to Traffic Control.

"He's being patched up in the casualty department at the hospital," said the York train control where Joe asked for news of Jim Simpson. "He won't be long he's not seriously injured. He's walking wounded - just. You go and camp out in the canteen on platform eight until he joins you."

Joe was ready for the canteen so he turned towards the door only to be arrested in his flight by the call of the controller. "I'd forgotten you and your mate are due to work the six-five Castlebrough. Stay in the canteen where I can get you on the phone, like as not you'll have to work it back with another driver."

A warm meat pie and a large mug of hot milky tea waited appetisingly on the scrubbed deal table where the supposed 'Aunt Betty' had placed it. She had passed the time of day with Joe but did not recall him as 'the fireman of last year from the London train who owed her for two meat pies'. Joe didn't enlighten her either, not that he intended to be dishonest but the error had happened so long ago that it would be embarrassing to recall it and explain why he had not been in and settled the account.

"Thanks," said Joe and paid the four pence required for the present food. There were few men in the canteen, consequently Joe had been privileged and was treated to conversation and individual service. The chat would not have to last long, Joe decided, because he didn't feel very good so he asked for three aspirins. Also his latest reading material was burning a hole in his pocket and a read would make him feel better.

"Now then Wade, me ole son." A heavy hand struck Joe cheerfully between the shoulder blades and jarred his throbbing head. Joe didn't respond with pleasure, he blurted out some tea and partly chewed pie and nearly choked as the voice continued. "How are yuh Joe? Been to a rodeo show lately? Sit up man and get yuh tea properly, slouching there won't do you any good."

Joe had sensed, and felt the presence of the loud Rusty Iron who irritated Joe even more by placing his aggressively muscular figure on the form alongside him. "I'll join yuh son." The fellow's exuberance and unstoppable conversation rasped in to Joe's aching head.

His vocal dominance was stopped briefly by Aunt Betty's interruption. "Have you any news about the crash?" she asked.

"What crash?" asked Joe.

"Just outside York. The injured are in York General."

"I heard summat," Rusty burst in un-invited. "Derailment at Strensall, I think they said. Where's Strensall?" Rusty shrugged, his thick neck and prominent ginger hair provided the justification for his name Rusty.

"I thought everybody knew where Strensall was?" Joe asked with a note of impatience but didn't wait for a reply. "Yes, it was Strensall. An engine lost a tyre."

"Was it punctured?" jerked in Rusty feeling sure he'd asked a funny question.

"An express came off the rails, lost a wheel they say." Betty interjected excitedly. "Doing 70 miles per hour. Coaches damaged. No one killed. Ten injured in hospital. Awful shock for those folks." She was the one with the up to date information. "The line's closed, the line to Castlebrough. Hey you, our Rene. Have you heard anymore about that crash?"

"I know about the crash," said Joe. "It was my train." He played the news down by speaking slowly and quietly. He feared his bit of news might cause an over reaction from Rene and Betty. There was already enough excitement and of course false rumour. "A large part of the trailing driving wheel broke up while we were travelling fast through Strensall. It smashed through the cab and did a lot of damage to the engine and two front coaches."

"What about the injured? They say there's injured in the hospital." Rene had joined and added her excitement as well as an unrequested pie in front of Joe.

"Not many, as far as I know. I thought there was only my mate, the driver, and me with this scratch I never told no one about."

"You never told. Let's have a look." Rusty was in again. "Don't look much. Like yuh cut yourself shaving."

"No it ain't much. That's why I didn't go to the hospital. I was a bit roughed up though. Knocked about, more like, as the engine bucked the rails." He sought to change the subject. "What you doing here in York in you're glad rags Rusty? Not fishing obviously."

"Fishing for a job. That's what. Just had a medical with the railway quack for a job on the loco's with you."

Joe experienced an involuntary shudder. The thought of tolerating this 'friendly' thug as a regular work-mate at the shed didn't appeal to his sense of humour.

"What exactly happened at the crash?" asked Betty. "You answer that phone Rene," she added as an aside to her helper as the bell sounded. "What happened?" she repeated to Joe.

"You know really, just what we've said so far. It was raining heavens hard and we were crackin' on from Flaxton to Strensal. Nice road there, slightly downhill and we were doing a nice seventy. She was a rough rider, tossing about a bit, but she was always like that. I was over at the fireman's side, just been talking to my mate, and I stepped over and put my head out. Looking for signals because of the rain and the black sky it wasn't easy to see. There was nowt on the line. The engine became noisier. Suddenly the side of the blinking cab came in, I felt the wooden step under my feet kick me upwards towards my mate. The floor came up. Then it was me and Jim hugging up to each other in the driver's corner. Jim had the brakes full on, we thought we were coming off the lines. If we had it would have been a crash."

"They want you across at Train Control," burst in Rene back fresh from her telephone duty.

"Bet you thought you'd had it," offered Rusty after an enforced silence while Joe had held the stage.

"Don't seem to remember thinking much. Funny thing is that time seemed to stand still, like a photograph."

"Shock, that's what that was," said the Aunty Betty figure.

Rene interrupted to deliver the rest of her telephone call. "Your driver's out of the hospital and he's coming to join you here. Here, will you have a cup of tea and another pie."

"Get a tea and pie for his driver," instructed Aunty Betty.

"An' for me too," loudly asked the omnipresent Rusty. He wasn't surprised to be ignored.

As they finished their tea and pies, Jim Simpson came in. Rene continued to Joe, "They want you over there. Quickly!"

"Can't he have his tea first?" asked Joe."

"I've had some." replied Jim. "We've got to be off."

Joe pocketed the pies for later and went off with Jim limping over the footbridge. Joe deviated to Train Control, while Rusty helped Jim down the steps. Joe went on and learnt the not surprising news that a York driver was waiting to meet up with him on platform nine, together he and the York driver had to work the six-five to Castlebrough. This was the train that Jim and Joe were booked to work. The only difference now was that Jim had been relieved by the York driver and that Rusty Iron was for ever present and talking. Joe was far from being enthusiastic. In fact, he felt dreadful.

"Looks a right load of crap," Joe said in anger, to the crew who brought the train and the K3 locomotive from Manchester for him to work to Castlebrough.

"Tis," said the blackened perspiring fireman. "You're very welcome to it," he said as he left the cab and grinned. "No doubt you've had one like it before."

"Do you're best old son," encouraged Jim Simpson. "You never got around to telling me the result of your Dad opening that letter and the Ukrainian bloke that was going to kill you."

"I told my Dad that she was my girl friend. Not the woman writing the letter. That was Katiya's Ma. He said that I shouldn't get mixed up with foreigners. I said she was alright, only wanted a chance. She's a clever lass, speaks all those languages. Said I'd bring her up home for them to see her. But my Dad say's 'you won't. I don't want any big Ukrainian guy coming here to kill you. Get yerself an English lass, or stay away from all of them'."

"Was that the end of it then?"

"I still see Katiya when I can. Her Ma still says, 'Ukrainish man get you' and she passes her hand across her throat. But I don't go down any back alleys in the dark without having a good look around." He parted from Jim, who struggled on his heavily bandaged leg to his passenger seat on the train. Joe made to mount the K3 locomotive.

★ ★ ★ ★

2
TOO TYRED.

"She's all yours pal. Yuh welcome." The Manchester crew's words echoed around Joe's aching head.

Joe understood why when he looked at the blue 'camel's hump' placidly occupying the centre of the firebox. "I couldn't make bloody toast on here," he exasperated. The boiler front was soot covered. Many of the steel control handles and wheels were rusty, a sure sign that the engine had been in store for a long time and had been brought out in emergency for traffic at a time when it was not fit. Coal was scattered over the cab floor and the slekker pipe was leaking steam and water all the time, the tap refused to be turned off. Not often did Joe feel fed up with his engine but he did this time. 'It's a bloody disgrace,' he said in his own head. 'The firing shovel's bent. The coal's all small wet slush. The water in the boiler is filthy and fizzing like mad, a sure sign she's going to prime like hell'.

"Better get summat done about it," retorted the York driver. There was no expressed sympathy in the spoken words of the tall thin driver or on his sharp, lined, facial features. His face looked as though it had forgotten how to smile. Maybe it had never known how to.

"I've a bloody good mind not to go," said Joe feeling rebellious. He felt tired, his throat and head hurt. He would like to have said to someone that he felt as though he was starting with a cold, but the driver was not likely to respond sympathetically to such a remark. "This engine ain't fit to work a train with."

"Get on with it," responded the driver in a monotone. "We're off in eight minutes. Won't get to Castlebrough by just moaning."

"I'll do it for you Joe. If you can't manage." The words were spoken by big Rusty, he'd just entered the cab. Surprisingly he was decked out in an L.N.E.R. locoman's cap and a dirty overall jacket. "Looks rough mate. If I knew the road I'd take it for you but I'm just learning it. I'll just get over there on the fireman's seat and keep out of the way."

The lanky, harass-faced driver ignored him, he looked too miserable to say 'good afternoon'. Joe knew of drivers who were very withdrawn to the point of being unfriendly but he'd never been with one that was so obviously depressed and unresponsive. The fellow remained silent except when he was forced by circumstance to speak. The footplate was a small confined space, a place of stresses and strains at the best of times but it was a terrible place when you had to share it and its responsibilities with an unfriendly mate. Joe's heart was heavy in his chest and butterflies threatened his stomach. 'Come on, Jim,' he appealed inaudibly to Jim Simpson on the train. 'Get on here and give me a help,' but such thoughts were forlorn. It added to his misery to see big Rusty sitting on the fireman's seat. 'Where ever did that big lout get the idea to pass himself off as a locoman learning the signals to Castlebrough? Where did he get that cap and jacket?' Joe couldn't say anything, he couldn't risk having to work with Rusty afterwards if he informed the driver of the masquerade, but then the sullen fellow seemed to be disinterested in Joe's problems.

There were ten minutes in which to fill the boiler, to make the fire burn more efficiently and get a full head of steam. His blower was working full blast, both injectors were on, Joe was deliberately depressing the steam pressure by filling the boiler to stop the driver starting away before the engine was ready. He levelled the fire with the long shovel, raised some clinker from the middle of the firebed and transferred it to the back corners and then fired selectively with small amounts of coal. He ignored Rusty who, tired of making ignored comments, fell silent. The minutes ticked by remorselessly. Sweat ran down Joe's face, his head pounded on the right side where he'd received a bump and the plaster-covered cut on his face smarted and irritated.

Fortunately the train was held after its departure time. When the guard's whistle was finally heard the driver dutifully sounded his engine whistle to mark his reply and warn those about that he was going to move. Joe had a full head of steam, the bark at the chimney top and the rush of steam from the open cylinder cocks marked their departure loudly.

The engine wheels slipped violently and the blast brightened the fire. Joe knew immediately that he had a mate who would thrash the engine madly without any thought of the fireman, he'd seen it before; no science, just brawn on the regulator and a quick hand to apply the brake. 'A flaming rough driver and a rotten engine. Just my luck,' thought Joe.

He did his best but the miles passed and steam and water fell. Haxby slipped by while they still pulled hard up the slight incline. A distant signal was at caution and the steam had to be shut off. Joe prayed that his unknown mate would not apply the brake and lose momentum unnecessarily. He didn't, but he opened her up and she roared the message to Joe that his coal was rapidly disappearing up the chimney. Joe was tired and dispirited, his usual optimism had deserted him.

At Strensall all the signals were at danger, a flagman waved the train on at caution and it proceeded slowly through the small-town station. The damaged D49 number 2758 and the two shattered coaches were unattended in the sidings. The broken wheel, crumbled cab-side and missing connecting rods were much in evidence. The sight prompted Rusty to start talking loudly. The York driver maintained his disinterested silence and they coasted slowly through Strensall. Joe looked around for signs of the damage the engine had inflicted when the wheel had broken, the ballast had been redistributed by the platelayers but marks on the wooden sleepers were obvious.

The train cleared the station and was away again. The rugged badly maintained K3 locomotive rolled and cracked, doing everything reluctantly and with the greatest inefficiency. It strained noisily to build up speed, the regulator was wide open and the engine was on low cut-off, the exhaust beats were uneven, it used steam and water very quickly, the fire was burning badly and could not replace the used steam pressure. The pressure fell, the water level fell, the driver was forced to close the regulator. They coasted slowly while the engine gathered some power into her belly. Once they stopped for five minutes, and to Joe the five minutes lasted an embarrassing age. Passengers gazed wonderingly out of the windows. Joe felt as though he were to blame. The driver said little, his attitude was one of total indifference. Joe was relieved to be left to his own devices, it was better than being constantly interfered with and irritated by the driver. As they approached the home board at Kirkham Abbey station the driver suddenly spoke, "We'll stop here and ask for assistance or another engine at Malton." He halted his locomotive opposite the Kirkham signal cabin and shouted his request to the signalman.

The struggle to Malton was embarrassing for Joe but there was little he could do. His one relief on the journey had been the quiet non-involvement of their uninvited passenger Rusty, who remained completely silent, so uncharacteristically silent that it was eerie. Joe could only assume that Rusty was remaining silent rather than risk exposing the subterfuge that he was a driver learning the road. They pulled into Malton station platform and a J27 six-coupled locomotive in Whitby bay platform joined them as a double-header. When they pulled away from Malton, Rusty Iron was not on the footplate, he had taken the opportunity to silently return to the coach and join Jim Simpson. Progress to Castlebrough was at a more normal speed but they lost forty minutes on the fifty-eight minute journey from York.

Relief flooded over Joe as they ran slowly into number one

platform at Castlebrough. But he was tired, his pains dominated his body and he was extremely black and sweat-drenched. He looked from his engine cab at the passengers leaving the train and chose not to leave the engine.

"That was a rough trip kiddo," the voice of Rusty invaded his peace of mind. "How often is it like that?" he went on to ask.

"Lots," replied Joe, as his driver looked on miserably from the cab towards Rusty. "You've got changed quickly. Where did you go at Malton?"

"Into the train." said Rusty but didn't display any wish to explain further. "I'm in a rush Joe. I'll push off." As he did so Jim Simpson limped up and said, "I'm going straight home from here. Tell the shed I'll be off work for a few days. You've seen Rusty have you? He says he wouldn't have your job at double the wage. Too bloody miserable on there he said."

"Okay," said Joe preparing to leave the cab but then he saw the blonde wirey hair of Katiya. She looked smart, more attractive than previously Joe thought. She was well dressed in a fur coat Joe had never before seen, she was taller because of high heeled shoes that were new to Joe. His impulse was to join her briefly but he quickly realised that she was being met by very close friends, obviously Ukrainian friends. The extremely long lasting warm embrace between her and a smooth faced smart young man irritated him. He stepped back into the shadows of the cab.

Joe experienced mixed emotions to see her embracing the man. He felt angry and envious. "Am I jealous?" he asked himself slightly audibly but so his miserable mate couldn't hear. "I can't be. I don't love her, I think I don't. I've never loved anyone." Despite his self assurances, he felt angry and hurt. She'd said 'Ich leibe Dich, mein leibling,' to him but he took it she was teaching him German. He felt so tired and aches troubled him in many parts of his body and he felt unusally anxious.

For diversion he turned to the tall silent figure of his York driver, intending to speak. The driver seemed to hover, spirit-like, in the corner of his cab, clutching the controls and waiting for whistled instructions. No words emerged from Joe's lips, no words were likely to emerge from the driver. 'The miserable beggar,' Joe thought, 'He's hardly spoken half a dozen times to me. What a lousy day it's been.' His spirits slumped as pains spread to further parts of his body.

★ ★ ★ ★

3
TYRED OUT.

Arrival at the shed brought him little relief. He was able to pass his scruffy, unfit engine over to someone else to clean and stable. His York driver made off without any acknowledgement to catch the eight o' clock express to York and his home.

Rusty Iron had at least improved matters by disappearing at the station. Now it was time for Joe to go home, 'spruce up' and go somewhere more pleasurable for the remaining evening hours. But did he feel well enough? He walked down the interior of the darkening shed where Jack Mild was lighting the shed gas lamps. Joe resolved to have a quick rub in the new wash basin to remove at least some of the grime from his face, and forget all about Katiya. If she'd got another bloke there was nothing he could do about it. The problem with her and her mother could wait until tomorrow evening when he'd meet her as she left her work at the Lilly White Laundry. The shed was quiet; the huge coal fire that was used to light the fires of the locomotives was crackling noisily and casting firelight into the darkening shed, no one was about, it was quiet for eight o' clock in the evening. Joe moved towards the messroom door where he was keen to see if he was still rostered on the 7 a.m. York goods for the morrow. A voice rang out as soon as his foot fell on the freshly sanded floor.

"You should have had more sense than let them make you bring that train from York," Tom West greeted him aggressively as he appeared.

Joe was taken aback by the venom in the question. "Did I have a choice?" Joe was honest with his question. He had not considered the possibility of refusing to fire the K3 from York on the train for which he was the rostered fireman.

"Course you did? You'd just been involved in a major accident with a passenger train which almost resulted in loss of life. Don't they teach you anything in that N.U.R? If I'd been with you, you'd have never got on an engine 'till you'd been declared fit. An' that'd be another day, not the same day. Simpson should have instructed you."

"I was alright. I'm home and okay?"

"You were injured, and in shock. You should never have got aboard that K3. You were short of steam. You had to get a Malton engine out to assist you. Have you no damned sense?"

Joe reacted angrily. He didn't expect a public roasting in the messroom from the father of his best mate. "Nobody could have done better with that engine. She was clinkered up, an' priming."

"You should have refused it Joe." The advice came from Johnny Marsay who was in a quiet huddle with a fireman further down the messroom.

"Why? It was my job."

"You've broken established practices. You've let your mates down."

"I, hell as. Rubbish."

"I thought there was more class solidarity in you Joe," remonstrated Johnny Marsay. "Anyway how are you? The plaster on your face, is that from the tyre coming off?" Then, before Joe could respond Johnny continued. "There's been a couple of chaps in trilbies looking for you earlier on."

"What's this about class solidarity? Bloody rubbish," came back Joe angrily. "What's that got to do wi' me bringing that train back."

"I'll tell yuh." Tom West rose quickly from his seat and his arms flailed in the usual manner as he scrunched across the sanded floor. If Joe hadn't known him very well he would have felt threatened by his approach. Tom spoke loudly. "Two month's ago Jim Cargill at Wetherby wouldn't take a train out after being in an accident, and the gaffer's suspended him for a week. The shed was going to stop work, the fellows were so mad. The men won, but the gaffers say they's the ones that decides. You should have known. Simmy should 'ave known. You've almost blacklegged, son. You'll have to do better next time."

Joe smarted. He felt guilty, as though he'd committed a grave error. He nodded in mute agreement. He knew about the strong feeling of solidarity that existed in the ranks of footplate men. They and their forbears had fought bitter struggles to obtain their present conditions and work according to specific agreements. After his mute assent he turned towards Johnny Marsay and the young fireman near the lockers at the end of the messroom.

"This suit you Joe? A week in a Summer School at Ruskin College, Oxford?" asked Johnny.

"Yuh mean spend me week's annual holiday in college?"

"If you wish to go on your holiday, you can. You get the week off work and subsistence, pocket money," said the unknown fireman in response to the quizzical look on Joe's face. "It's a union sponsored course. You get your keep, your fare and your fees paid. All you have to do is study and talk. I'm Bob Rugton," he continued, "Area Council Secretary, Men's Side. I get the forms from A.S.L.E.F. to pass on to likely lads. You've done a few of the National Council of Labour College Courses, Johnny says."

"Yeh. Three. Chairmanship, Elementary Arithmetic and Public Speaking."

"You're just the lad," said Bob Rugton.

"But wait a minute. You said A.S.L.E.F., I'm N.U.R."

"No problem. It doesn't matter if you are a calithumpian as long as you are in a T.U.C. affiliated union."

"I'll have it if it's going free. I hand it in to my N.U.R. branch secretary do I?" Joe noted the nodded assent and added, "I'm about to start an N.C.L.C. public speaking course taught by Jim Simpson."

"Don't mention the N.U.R. too many times," said Johnny with a laugh, "It leads to bad feeling."

"You said earlier that someone had been looking for me. Hope it weren't the long face driver I've just come in with from York. Long-faced sod. I've just had the worst day in my life."

"No. He's 'Misery Mac', Bob Mackintosh. His wife makes him miserable like that they say," explained Bob the York fireman. "There's plenty of York firemen won't travel with him."

It was Johnny who completed the information about the two men. "There was two guys at the gate, half way down the steps. Both in trilbies. I asked them if they wanted someone. They said 'Yes, Josef Wade', They were kind of foreign, like, didn't speak proper English, yet they were talking alright." said Johnny.

"Don't know no one like that." Joe was firm about that but it didn't stop him considering whether it could be the mother's Ukrainian friend."

"You alright Joe?" asked Johnny. "You look about done in."

"Think you're right. I really am done in. Do you think I could be in shock?"

"Sure will be," volunteered the York fireman. "You don't often lose a tyre at seventy. When you do, an' I ain't heard on it before, I reckon it squeezes the crap out of you."

"I reckon you're right. It were like a bloody bomb going off under the cab. Yer right. It frightened the crap out of me. Threw us all over the place? Nearly threw us off the road." Joe went on to recount the event in greater detail than he thought he had recorded at the time. This time he felt some emotion surfacing and he registered some fear to relate to the event. His feet hurt, they throbbed, he recalled he'd felt the upward thrust of the wheel as it struck the boards he was standing on, that was when he'd jumped at Jim. Tremor vibrated outwards from his heart, he felt weak. He moved to sit on the bare wooden bench. "I do feel beggared Johnny. Must be shock. I feel exhausted."

"Go home. Get to bed. Have that cut looked at. I'll come with you if my mate can wait while I come back."

"I'm alright kidder," said Joe softly. "I'll just go up to the 'Tavern' and have a drink. Then go home." He went off feeling tired and unsure, accompanied as far as the gate by his mate Johnny. Then after a hesitating re-think he decided to struggle on to the 'Railway Tavern'. He leaned on the bar, there were few men drinking even though the hour was past eight 'o clock, He drank half a glass of mild beer, closed his eyes to steady himself, felt his arms tremble and heard nearby voices speaking an eastern language. He didn't need to turn and look, from the corner of his eye he saw the two men whom Johnny had described as asking for him. He tried to drink but felt an overwhelming weariness. His eyes closed and his legs just let him slide to the floor.

His eyes opened onto the whitewashed ceiling of the bedroom he shared with his brother. His face felt unwashed, he could tell that someone had tried to wash his face, his hands also. He looked at them. They were partly washed. But he was in his own bed. His eyes closed again. Then he heard his Mother's voice. "Are you better yet Joseph?"

"Yes Mam. I'm tired. How did I . . ." The darkness slipped away and the sun poured in through the window. His younger brother Luke looked in through the open door, "You better yet Joe?" he asked and then the veil of darkness slid in over Joe again. It lifted and a call registered on his lips. "Mam" he was muttering. "Can I have something to eat?"

"I've been telling you to get more sleep. You're tired out. Fancy fainting in the Tavern. It's four days since you collapsed." His mother was accounting for the missing hours and days. He didn't think he'd fainted. "Women faint." he said. He'd been out like a light for a long time. His throat hurt like Hell. "Feel like I've got the flu' Mam," he said. "Can I get up for a proper wash." Strangely, he felt closer to his mother when he was ill. 'Why don't I think like this when I'm not poorly. I need a Mam all the time. I'll stop running off out every time I've got chance to be at home'. Bed claimed him for two weeks until his influenza was sweated out of him and his quinseys were lanced. Joe dreaded the thought of going back to work because Tom West would play hell with him again and say that what had happened had proved his point. He would repeat his earlier advice that Joe should not have fired that K3 from York to Castlebrough after the accident.

1
Nightmare in the snow

"Evenin' Sir," spoke the ticket collector. "Goin' to be a white Christmas, it seems like."

Doctor Earnshaw grunted a response from his hooded coat, he didn't mean to be disinterested in the greeting and comment. When he realised that he'd been addressed and hadn't replied he faltered in his stride and stepped back a pace to respond in his usual friendly manner. "Sorry, I had my head in the clouds, in my coat-hood more like." He shook his frame and long coat, snow fell from him to the ground. He was away from the driving snow and beneath the roof-cover of Castlebrough Station and now there was time to respond, it was only a quarter-to-eight in the evening. "The weather's foul," he said. "So very sudden, all this snow. Could be set for a white Christmas." He continued, "I left my car and went for a bus, but there's no services. They said the roads are impassable so I'd better go by train. That's what they're telling their passengers."

"Robin Hood's Bay," muttered the ticket collector on looking at the proffered ticket. "The eight o'clock Whitby's in two platform. You'll soon be at the Bay. And the train's warmer than a car or a bus on a night like this." He clipped the Doctor's ticket. "You also going to Whitby?" he said towards the young woman presenting her ticket next.

"Yes, the buses are off and I want to get home tonight," she replied. "I've been at work all day."

"You'll both be alright with the L.N.E.R. We always get through," replied the ticket inspector. "We run when others can't. In platform two, Miss. There's going to be a few extra passengers with this sudden snow."

"The wind's ferocious, I had to put my brolly down. It was blowing away," responded Miss Brown, who had likewise been directed to the railway station by the bus company.

"You get yourself on that warm train in number two, Miss. Just up there, see." He pointed, "You can see steam rising from the carriages. The engine's on, heating the train. You wouldn't get that comfort on your buses. Would yuh Miss?"

Doctor Earnshaw and Betty Brown, a young office worker, were inclined to agree as the heat met them when they opened a compartment door in the non-corridor, four-coach train. Through the wispy clouds of steam rising from the heaters on the train they could see a 'Woodley's Bakehouse' Bradford Jowett van unloading trays of cakes and bread into the guards van. Woodley's had planned an early morning road delivery of bakehouse products to their shop outlets in Whitby but were having to resort to rail. The early snowstorm was causing problems for goods and passengers in many parts of the country but it was also inflating the number of rail users in relation to road users. The incoming Hull connection brought a Royal Air Force sergeant, on week-end leave, hurrying to make his Whitby link. The crew on the Whitby G5 side-tank locomotive awaited the whistle and flag that would send them on their way over the undulating but steep, coast railway line to Whitby.

Joe and Jimmy Woodley were nearby onlookers from their J27 locomotive in platform one where they were waiting for a passage to Castlebrough Shed. "We've enough foreigners in Britain looking for jobs without bringing more in," said Jim. "Won't be long before there's as much unemployment as there was before the war."

"Yes Jim, but these displaced persons have to settle somewhere. They're not only coming to Britain. Some are going to America, Canada, South Africa, Southern Rhodesia and Australia," Joe replied. "We've got to do our bit."

"Our bit starts at home." Jim was firm. He believed in safeguarding jobs for 'our sens'. "Anyway if any of them gets jobs offered on the railways you can bet the unions'll oppose them. We've learnt that we've got to look after our jobs."

"The paper lists, mining, building, farm work and quarrying as areas where labour is short, and the Government is going to pay to get displaced persons settled where they can help Britain with her rebuilding."

"They should be at home rebuilding their own countries. Anyway they aren't as good as us. You're only talking like this 'cos you've got that girl friend who's one of them. They're backward. You haven't to forget that Britain's got the biggest and best empire ever known. We wouldn't have done that if we hadn't been superior people."

Joe decided to change the subject. He could understand the concerns about foreigners 'taking our jobs' but it didn't seem correct for displaced persons not to be given jobs and homes in Britain. "Whitby's leaving two platform, Jim, then we can get to the shed. We'll be lucky to get finished by ten tonight. We've still got three engines to deal with."

★ ★ ★ ★

In spite of the thick white blanket of snow and the whiteness of the driving blizzard, a blackness shrouded the eight o'clock Castlebrough to Whitby train on its last journey of the day. The only exception was where compartment electric light and the engine's firelight danced on the trees, fences and the lineside snow-covered banks. The driving snow fell through the shafts of light and visibility was very restricted.

The days of blacked-out trains were gone. The war was over, plans for peace and change for the better dominated people's minds, there was a burning expectation that things would, indeed had to, get better. Woe betide anyone who stopped things from improving, and yet there were homeless families impatiently squatting in empty properties, there were food shortages, coal shortages, scheduled electricity cuts and low gas pressure and a whole host of other privations. The war had been finished for three months, there had been a political electoral revolution and a torrent of promises. Strikes on the railways in the North-West had won a 44 hour week, two weeks annual holiday and a pay increase for all railwaymen but things were not really getting better quickly enough on the home front.

"Snow's lying thick mate. Thought that drift were going to stop us." The Whitby driver on the G5 locomotive spoke to his fireman as they both peered from the cab. The small but powerful side-tank locomotive exhausted noisily and rolled as it climbed uphill towards Stainton Dale. Hot coals shot into the night sky from the chimney to disappear into the blizzard and the darkness.

"Yeh, she dragged a bit. It'll be worse the other side of Stainton Dale," the fireman replied.

"There's the station lights," replied Sid. Only a few month's ago the station lights would have been almost non-existent because of black-out regulations.

They rolled into the platform at Stainton Dale and saw a uniformed figure and two passengers huddled in the shelter of the Booking Office doorway. As their train ground slowly around the curve of the station platform the uniformed figure of Station Master Reginald Barr advanced in the swiftly blowing snow towards the moving locomotive. The waiting passengers hung back while the train came to a halt. The station master was advancing towards the engine with the hooped tablet on his arm, He climbed aboard the closed and side-sheeted cab of the G5 tank loco.

"Rough night tonight Sid. Did you have any trouble coming up?"

"Not really, bit thick in Crinkle Bottom. Alus is when there's a bit of snow. Slowed us, but didn't stop us," replied the Whitby driver.

"If you got through there you shouldn't have much trouble the rest of the way. That bit's alus the worst," responded the station master.

"Yes but it's still snowing. Could block us in at Midge Hole.

Depends on the wind," replied the small driver. His size was noticeable because it was obvious that he was just below the minimum regulation height of five feet four inches. Most locomen were taller and this made small men outstandingly noticeable. Few were less than the minimum height and usually there were special reasons why they were employed. One of the more usual reasons was that if the man had been taken on in one of the war periods when labour was scarce he was likely to be kept on in the following peace time. Sid was one such person. He had joined the railway service during the carnage of the First World War before being called into the army where he earned a bravery award and some unusual wounds. His union and a sympathetic management kept him at his job. Providing he was able to reach the controls he would be able to do his job if he was also strong enough. Being employed at Whitby locomotive shed helped his case because he was unlikely to have to work on really big locomotives like Pacifics, V2s or W.D. loco's.

Reginald Barr pulled himself into the warmth of the cab and presented the tablet for the line section to Ravenscar. The driver warily examined it to ascertain that it gave him permission to drive into the section of line that led to Ravenscar. "You've only two passengers from here to Ravenscar. One of 'em's Blaster Baines," said Reg Barr. "Tanked up t' eyeballs an cheeky wi' it. He's had a bit off to the other passenger who's a lady. I'm going to put him in the first compartment next to the engine an' her in another one. Can you see that he get's off at Ravenscar?" The station master left the cab and hurried back into the blizzard to catch the arm of Blaster Baines. He confirmed that the two carriage door handles were secure after the two passengers had boarded the train, then held his green lamp aloft to signal to the guard that the train was free to depart.

The climb to the top of Ravenscar peak was hazardous in the howling blizzard. The engine worked hard on a low cut-off to create maximum effort. Thick, drifting snow, blanketed the rails and threatened to clog the wheels and bring the train to a halt, but forward motion kept them pressing onwards and upwards until they passed the barely visible home signal on its tall post on the approaches to Ravenscar Station. The track levelled off and they ran to a halt alongside the down-line wooden platform.

The fireman, took the hooped tablet from its hanging place on the handbrake, departed the cab and set off to meet the signalman who had not yet left his cabin. The station paraffin lamps glowed in the storm which blew savagely across the exposed six-hundred feet high headland on which Ravenscar was sited. Only the shrouded lady left the train. Ernest ran back to rouse the inebriated Blaster. The door opened to reveal him, horizontal, in the dimly lighted compartment, on the bench type seat. "Out Blaster! Your stop. And don't get lost in the snow."

Blaster did not arouse. Ernest went into the compartment and hauled him to his feet and the wind and the snow flurried in his face and made him recoil. "Come on old son. You've got to get off." Blaster rose to struggle though the storm assailed doorway. "I'm going to the cabin to pick up the tablet," Ernest said, "Shut the door when you leave." then he left at a run through the ankle high snow, down the platform to exchange the tablet in the cabin on the other platform.

"Sorry," said the porter signal, who rounded the end of the platform with head bowed and almost collided with Ernest, "I was taken up on the telephone as you entered the station." He changed tablets with Ernest, who turned towards his engine.

"Anything wrong?" asked Ernest in response.

"Only this damned blizzard, an' the cold. It's really cold. Everything's frozen up," said the porter signalman. "The Robin Hood's Bay signalman wants you to crack-on. He can go home when you clear Prospect Hill, You're ten minutes late and he's waiting to go to the Club and Institute."

The fireman assured him that they'd make that time up as they ran down the three mile of track to Robin Hood's Bay. As he arrived at his loco with the tablet he glanced at the door handle where Blaster had been. It was secure. The guard's green lamp was twinkling through the blizzard to authorise the driver to depart. The loco whistle popped in acknowledgement and the regulator valve drew steam for the cylinders and the journey into the night began. Sid was a driver that liked to make his train accelerate away from a station with maximum speed. The chimney roared in salute to his efforts to move forwards quickly and the train dipped smartly downhill into the cutting that led them into Ravenscar Tunnel. Little could be seen except for the badly lighted advance semaphore signal that guarded the approach into the long section down into Robin Hood's Bay Station. The tunnel swallowed them and the firelight danced on the shiny wet sides of the tunnel. The noise of the train grinding around the curve of the lines filled the tunnel with a cacophony of sound which drowned speech but was an expected part of any steam train journey through a tunnel.

In spite of the driving sleet, when they emerged from the lower end of the tunnel they could see the twinkle of the sea in the huge bay, and enough light dressed the falling escarpment for some of its snow-covered features to mark themselves out on the landscape. The line was swept clear by the wind on suitably exposed portions of the track-bed but in cuttings and close to small embankments the snow had formed significant deep drifts.

"There goes another one," shouted Sid as he opened his regulator and put steam into the cylinders to break through a choking white drift. "We're through," he shouted as the engine wheels spun and they broke through to a clearer section of line down which he could allow his train to coast until they hit the next drift. Not often was it necessary to drive downhill, but it was tonight in some parts, and Ernest had to bend his back to replenish his fire and steam.

Fyling Hall station passed by and Robin Hood's Bay came upon them out of the trees. The station lamps revealed the double tracked station sorely impeded by drifting snow. The chimney top of the G5 barked as Sid drove hard at the bank of snow that piled against the platforms. He was through. He stopped and wondered whether he would manage to start again. "We'll shovel some of the snow clear of the wheels before we kick off," he addressed his fireman Ernest. He said 'we' but Ernest knew that he meant him.

Some passengers including the jolly Doctor Earnshaw left the train and one joined it. Ernest was helped to clear the snow by the station master and the porter signalman who were keen to see this last train of the day arrive at Prospect Hill Whitby. They would then close Robin Hood's Bay Station for the night and go their private ways.

With their passage eased slightly by the removal of some snow, and with their sanding equipment helping them to grip the rails, they successfully started off on the last lap. Up the gently rising gradient they fought the drifts in the teeth of an intensifying north-easterly blast. They slowed, then they broke through. The driver used his detailed knowledge of the line and his years of driving experience to master the adverse conditions.

"Hawsker cutting's our last big problem. We'll hit it soon," shouted Sid over the noise of the slipping engine wheels and the December blast as they approached the cutting. The snow was deep, feet deep, its cotton-wool embrace clogged their wheels and confounded all their efforts and they were brought to a halt. No strategy could move the train either forward or in reverse. "We aren't stopping here," said Sid to his fireman. "Get down and loose off. We'll uncouple and run forward light and break a passage through."

The fireman opened his cab side-door and moved the tarpaulin sheet that kept most of the driving snow and wind out of the cab. He backed himself out into the night and down the steps of his cab. His driver watched his progress. "The snow's hellish deep," Ernest shouted upwards, through the darkness and the wind, towards the protruding face of his mate. He stepped out onto the snow and sank into its icy grasp, his legs almost totally submerged. "Gimme me shovel Sid?"

The task seemed almost impossible.With his legs almost buried in the snow he moved enough to make a passage to the engine coupling beneath the train. "Don't you come down Sid," he shouted up through the storm as he compacted snow with blows of his shovel to take his weight. He detached the engine at the moment he heard the cry in the storm. A compartment door clicked somewhere above his head and something fell heavily on the nearby snow.

"It's damned Blaster. He never got off at Ravenscar," the fireman said to himself as he struggled towards the prostrate figure in the snow and shouted, "He's fallen out of the train. Sid, can you come and give me a hand?"

"I'm here too - the guard," cried another voice in the storm. "Can you come here to help us John?" yelled the fireman. "Give me a hand to get Blaster Baines on his feet."

Together they struggled to make the drunken Blaster upright. "We'd better try and get him up on the engine, to warm him through," said Ernest. "He'll manage with help, I hope." They hauled his short bulk upwards into the cab like a bag of wheat being dragged through a first-floor mill-loading bay and propped him up on the fireman's seat and then discussed what was to be done.

"We're going to break through the snow with the engine. Mek a path and then come back for the train." The driver gave his instructions. "You made her ready didn't you Ernest? You took the pipes off?" he asked, then opened the regulator quickly and made the engine wheels slip while in forward gear, then he reversed his engine and then squeezed up to the train and depressed the buffers as hard as he could, then into forward gear again. With the full regulator open and with impetus from the sprung buffers his engine moved forward and broke through the snow.

The inebriated Blaster sat up like a startled ghost caught in the firelight and yelled when the engine slipped wildly and surged forward. "Hold him," yelled the driver. "Don't let him fall out of the cab again." The locomotive moved forward from the train and gave the crew hope of breaking free. They advanced twenty yards closer to Whitby but then hit deeper clutching folds of wind-lashed snow and succumbed. Frantic efforts to return to the train were thwarted.

"It calls for a Council of War," Sid said ruefully. "There's no heating on that train now. An' the electric batteries aren't going to last long."

"It's a grim situation. I'll give you that," offered the guard trying to be helpful. "My Mother used to say if there's nowt you can do about summat, Just get your head down and make yourself warm. The Good Lord'll provide."

"But he ain't here," said Ernest.

"I'm here," muttered Blaster showing more signs of life.

"We know. You're just one more trouble." the driver returned ruefully. "We've got to think of the passengers. Better tell them what's happened and don't bloody well let any more fall out. Get 'em together in a small number of compartments. It'll keep them warmer. Tell 'em about the lights. If you can turn some of the lights off that'll help. Any other ideas. By the way move the young ones to join the elderly. Not the other way round."

"I've got an idea," said the guard with a grin. "There's a big consignment of Woodley's bread and cakes in the van. And a churn full of fresh milk. I'll tek it on meself to be responsible for dishing out rations. Milk'll do everybody good."

Blaster retched in reply.

"What about lavatories?" asked Ernest the fireman.

Blaster retched even more loudly. "I can't drink out of one of them."

"Yes, the passengers are bound to ask for a lavy and there isn't one on this train," responded the driver thoughtfully. "Best I can think of is let them use the milk churn lid in the van!"

Blaster punctuated with another retch.

"Lose him in the snow please," said Sid enthusiastically. "Come to think of it you can use the fire bucket in the van as a lavy. Better not use the milk churn lid." He turned his attention back to more immediate matters. "You two see what you can do with the passengers. Say sorry. We'll soon get help and get them on the way to Whitby. When you come back Ernest. I'm going to see if I can walk on to Hawsker."

"That's going to be risky in this storm. We're stranded on the Moors, Sid." The guard addressed them all. "An' you know what that can mean. I don't think you should leave the train."

★ ★ ★ ★

"We're asking them to pay you full wages for the three-week

period when you were off ill." Bill Branson was talking to Joe in the Castlebrough shed messroom. "It was an accident really and the L.N.E.R. were responsible for putting you in the situation which harmed you."

"But Bill, I know I had flu, and quinsies. An' I was suffering from some kind of delayed shock, Doctor Harker says. But I don't think I'd o' been off work with shock." Joe was responding to the local N.U.R's secretary's pressure to pursue a claim against the L.N.E.R.

"How often have you collapsed in a pub bar from flu? You know that the doctor said you were suffering from delayed concussion. Your only going to be asking for your three weeks' wages. Why so stubborn. Eh?"

"I'm not Bill. Just want to do the right thing."

"I do too. You know what Tom West's attitude is. If you'd been in A.S.L.E.F. you would never have been working that K3 back after the crash."

"Okay Bill. You know best. I'll put a claim in."

"You should have reported yourself injured and gone for a checkup."

"I did Bill. I had that cut on my face dressed."

"Out of the guard's emergency box. That's not attention. Why you didn't tell anyone about the knock on your head, I'll never know? Here get your monica on this form and let me get down to the Mere Social Club."

"Thanks for dropping in, Bill."

"I wouldn't have done if I hadn't been going to the Club. I don't make a habit of this sort of thing on a Friday night."

"Right thing you've done son," said Bill Clarke who was seated nearby on a messroom seat with Jim Woodley. "You were out cold in the Tavern. Why the doc didn't send you to hospital instead of home beats me. By the way Jim, don't you two go off home yet. Control say there's a train in trouble on the coast road, might need you to take the vans out."

Jim was furious. He had just washed up, made out his time sheet and lit his pipe and was on his way to the Railway Tavern. "You're bloody joking."

"You can't go yet. You're on pay, both of you. The night foreman comes on at ten. Go when he says okay. I can't tell you to go."

"We've done our whack, Bill. Got eight an' a half-hour's work in on the sheet ain't we Jim?" Joe had intervened in support of Jim Woodley.

"Can't help that. You're on pay until half-past one. There's no one else to call out. If Control asks for help you'll have to go. I'm saying nowt else except hang about 'til Frobisher comes then do what he says." Bill Clarke disappeared in the direction of his store office, he'd faced all the wrath from Jim he intended to face.

Jim fumed and paced up and down the sand-strewn floor cursing. "Well I'm going up to the Railway Tavern till eleven, you stay here and come up for me if we're needed."

"Okay Jim. I'll do that. We ain't got a head of steam in any engine in the shed if we're needed. I'd better see Bill and ask him which we'll take if we have to go."

Jim ignored Joe's helpful remark and pounded angrily through the door opening. Joe went to glean more news about the anticipated emergency on the coast road.

★ ★ ★ ★

"Yes, lady. We are stuck in the snow. There's no heat on the train so we want you to come down out of that compartment and join others in another compartment." Betty Brown had opened her window and had closed it quickly as the blizzard howled through the opening but she'd seen the figures below beckoning up to her. She heeded the message and the instruction. She was lifted down roughly and concealed her embarrassment to the best of her ability while she was carried through the deep snow and lifted up to join five ladies and two children in a compartment next to the van at the rear of the train. A single electric bulb drew power from the batteries and cast a weak yellow glow around the dull brown interior. The train's seven paraffin lamps had been lighted and were placed in the centre of the compartment to provide a little heat.

"Lady, can I have your ear a moment?" The guard beckoned to an older lady close to the door. She stooped and he whispered instructions about the primitive toilet provision. "Pass it on, the message I mean." He closed his mouth just before he almost jokingly added, "Not the w-w-water" but he cheerfully did add that he would be around with supper and a drink of milk later.

The six men in the next compartment did not warrant the same kind of deferential treatment. They had no heat from paraffin lamps but had the weak solitary electric light. They grumbled. The Air Force sergeant Jim Cameron announced that he would wait for half-an-hour and if they weren't rescued then he was going to walk to Whitby, "Snow or no snow." Warnings from others were of no avail. The train guard's message about the cakes and milk drew little enthusiastic

response. The advice about the fire-bucket in the guards van brought
a laugh about an attempt one of them had made to pass water through
the window into the teeth of the gale. "He got his own back," was the
laughter-accompanied remark. A single unexpected pop on the engine
whistle reminded them of their troublesome guest on the footplate.
The three of them struggled through the wind and the clinging snow
towards the engine.

"I've just seen a horse," bleated the sickly Blaster Baines looking
out from the cab. "Or it were a nightmare. Must've been a nightmare
'cos it spoke to me."

"What did it say?" asked Ernest. He was climbing up the side of
the cab.

"Horses don't talk. Only to drunks like you Blaster." Sid was
scrambling up into the cab.

"There was a horse's head pushing that sheet," he pointed to the
sheet-covered driver's side of the cab. "I didn't know what it was 'til
I pulled the sheet back. It snorted, a big cart hoss, an' it spoke. Said,
'We've found you'."

John the guard yelled from below at the side of the loco. "Here Sid.
There's a big hoss here." The big horse was ploughing through the
deep snow from the front end of the locomotive and as it came into
vision through the darkness and the snow-fall it displayed its two
riders - the station master from Hawsker and his neighbouring farmer.

"We've found you. Thanks for that," said one of the figures who
revealed himself to be the Hawsker station master.

The train crew gave a quick report and then the station master said,
"We'll get back quickly and get an engine out for you. Soon have you
back home. Everybody stay put. The snow is deeper than we've ever
seen it."

They were as good as their word, they alerted the Permanent Way
Inspector and Whitby locomotive sheds. An engine and van set out
from Whitby intent on breaking through to them but its determined
attempt was swallowed in the drifts. The rescue engine and van were
tight fast in the snow providing just one more obstacle between the
train and Whitby, proof, if proof were needed, that the snow in front
of the Whitby bound passenger train was very deep and widespread.
Sid, Ernest and John the guard reported to all the passengers.

The air force sergeant responded by pledging that he was going to
walk home. "I'm on weekend leave to see my wife and kids," he said,
"and I want a night in my own bed and not spending it frozen on a
train with a bunch of fellows. I'll get there alright." He stumbled off
into the darkness and the falling snow amid dire warnings. The rest

had to await a possible rescue from Castlebrough and hope that the sergeant would not perish in the snow.

★ ★ ★ ★

2
The Rescue.

Jim Woodley suddenly lost his affable mood when he saw Joe Wade come through the front door of the Railway Tavern. He didn't need to be told that the train at Whitby wanted assistance. His face blackened, he snapped at Joe as though it were his fault, "Eleven o' clock is no time to be going to Whitby. After a day's work, as well," Jim complained loudly as he departed his drinking friends.

"I got 9885 ready for us to take. She's facing the right way for coming back to Robin Hood's Bay. The fitter bolted the small snowplough onto the engine rear-end to help us get through. If I can get help I'll transfer it to the front-end for coming home if we need it. He showed me what to do."

"You have been a busy lad," Jim replied somewhat sarcastically. Joe knew it was the beer and the anger talking.

The snow and wind had abated a bit but the lines were still covered and snow-blocked points still being cleared. Jim Woodley and his 9885 side-tank were given a passage onto the Whitby line which had been kept open specially. The small snow-plough eased their passage. Jim Woodley suddenly surprised Joe with the instruction, "You've got enough fire on for a while haven't you? Well get hold of that regulator and give me time to have a smoke. All the boards should be off but keep your eyes skinned. Especially for unmanned crossings. I'll keep an eye on you from behind. We'll have the road to ourselves until we get to Robin Hood's Bay."

Joe didn't need a second invitation or instruction, he tingled with excitement, he'd dreamed about the day, now it was a reality. He wasn't driving the 'Castlebrough Flyer' but that didn't matter, he had to start somewhere. He stood proudly at the controls, looked out diligently, and opened and shut the regulator as the gradients demanded. He felt good, better because of the driving snow, he'd never driven before but he didn't tell that to Jim Woodley. He sped through the blackness and the falling snow, calling out all the signals, crossings, and speed restrictions to Jim. The only drifts of any significance were around Stainton Dale and Ravenscar but Joe stayed at the controls until they drew into Ravenscar then Jim said "I'll take her from here down the hill to Robin Hood's Bay."

Drifting was more evident as they travelled down the long escarpment, but they avoided trouble and pulled into Robin Hood's Bay station at one o'clock Saturday morning. With two platelayers and shovels they set off to find the train. The drifts halted them but they were able to back out, do a bit of digging and have another run and break through. When they arrived in the proximity of the train they had much snow to move but the weather was improving. Eventually they attached and tried to pull the train back but it moved only slightly, the whole train was stuck fast.

"Uncouple the first carriage Joe. We'll see if we can move them one at a time." They were successful, it moved slowly to the accompaniment of cheering passengers and train crew and started its journey back to Robin Hood's Bay. The small plough now fixed at the front end broke through the drifts. Without being halted and with the beat of the exhaust pounding into the night sky they challenged the slowly easing blizzard. The engine and the coach pulled into the platform at Robin Hood's Bay.

Joe left his engine quickly to be the first one to greet the passengers after their long confinement in the train. The men left in a rush and the ladies followed. The station master was attempting to address them as they emerged. "I'm going to take you all down to the Victoria Hotel were you can wash and get warm and have a sleep. Later they will prepare breakfast for you. We will be trying to get you to Whitby."

Joe's eyes were sweeping the tired shadowy faces of the passengers while he listened with Jim Woodley close behind him. Both were intent being in at this moment of rescue. The men emerged, a forestry worker with his own long-handled axe bounced out as though it was the middle of the day. He was quiet. Joe harboured the brief thought that the man might be the Ukrainian looking for him. He dismissed the thought because he had not seen Katiya since his accident. No one would be looking for him now.

He recognised someone. 'That's Carol,' he said to himself. He was surprised. 'Yes! It is Carol'. "It's Carol Blanchard," he said to Jim and went on to declare, "It's Carol who begged a lift with us through Kettleness Tunnel?"

"Don't know," responded Jim only partly interested in Joe's problem.

"She's got a soft woollen hat and a high collar. Yes it is her, Jim."

Joe moved after Carol as she followed the group. He caught her arm and pulled her around. Even in the dim station lamp light and from the rear it was clear to Joe that he had been correct, it was Carol Blanchard and she was one of the passengers. She recognised him and greeted him warmly, pleased again to be meeting. She spoke to Jim, who now remembered her escapade on engine 9885, the same engine they were using tonight. They talked until the party were led off, through the piled snow, in the direction of Victoria Hotel. She still lived at Whitby but her family were soon going to be living in Castlebrough she said. "Next week in fact." This was the last week-end when she would travel to Whitby to be at home.

"Maybe I'll see you in Castlebrough," she said to Joe.

"I hope so," Joe replied quickly and brightly. "I've got to go now. Jim's waving of me." She went on to the hotel while Joe and Jim set out to bring in the rest of the coaches, one at a time if necessary.

The same strategy recovered another carriage from the snow at Hawsker to take back to Robin Hood's Bay. They left the two men moving snow from the wheels of the remaining two. The next rescue attempt was also successful and the coaches moved free. As Jim prepared to leave for Robin Hood's Bay, the Whitby Permanent Way Inspector called up to him on the footplate. "I've still got two engines and a van blocking the line. Come back. I think I can see a way to release them all with your help."

"Can't stay. Sorry," said Jim. "We've got to get back to Castlebrough. They're waiting to close the line when we've got back."

"The line to Castlebrough from Robin Hood's Bay has been closed ever since you arrived here," replied the inspector "It'll open again at seven."

"Blast," responded Jim who prepared for a more wordy complaint. But the inspector intervened before Jim spoke.

"Get this done driver and there's drinks, bed, and breakfast at the Victoria for you till the road opens."

"Bloody Hobson's Choice, that's what you're giving me. You're saying, You can go home or stay but the line's closed so you've got to stay." Jim fumed but his options did not alter.

"Open this line for us driver and the passengers'll be able to get home by train. Failing that they'll have to wait 'til the road traffic can get through for them."

Jim produced a grudging assent. Joe was overjoyed by the news but he remained silent, his first thought had been the red-haired Carol who pleased him in a warm kind of way. 'I'll have chance to see her again and find out where she's going to live in Castlebrough,' he thought. They completed the journey from Hawsker to Robin Hood's Bay with the two coaches and then returned for the embedded G5 Whitby engine. The snow had stopped falling and the north-easterly blast had turned into a cold breeze. The plan was to attache themselves to the Whitby G5 and with it move forward to release the Whitby Permanent Way Inspector's engine and van.

Blaster Baines, who was still in the G5 cab with the Whitby crew was the last passenger to be rescued. With the gang, their engine broke through the long drift that blocked its way. They coupled to the G5, took Blaster on board at the express desire of the Whitby crew, who were tired of his tales, and cleared a way to the inspector's engine. The two engines coupled to the inspector's engine and took it forward to Prospect Hill on the outskirts of Whitby from where they travelled back to Robin Hood's Bay and breakfast through the high-walled drifts.

"Where's the Victoria Hotel?" asked Jim of the station master when they arrived at Robin Hood's Bay.

"I'll take you," he replied.

"Tie her down securely Joe. Don't want her to go walkies while we are in the hotel," instructed Jim.

"I'll be watching over her from my house. You get off down the road. You've earned it," encouraged the station master. He continued, "It's a quarter to three and the line's clear. Amazing."

Joe and Jim entered the Resident's Bar at the Victoria Hotel where the passengers were eating or drinking and were greeted like heroes, which in this company meant being offered a lot to drink. Joe was surprised by his driver's refusal to accept all the drink offered. "I've got to be sober for driving home at seven but I'll do my best to be obliging," he promised.

"It's my problem too," said the Whitby driver. "I've got to leave as soon as you passengers are ready."

"We're not going while there's a party on. All paid for by the London North Eastern Railway Company. I wonder if that RAF sergeant got home alright," offered one of the men.

"We want to go as soon as it's safe. Don't we Mrs Banner? We only went to the pantomime at Castlebrough with the kids. And we've had a right proper pantomime haven't we? Everybody has been so kind and helpful though."

"I think we ought to leave at seven," shouted the station master. "If you get there before that you'll not get busses or taxis. The L.N.E.R. will pay for the taxis. I've got all your addresses and I'll send a claim form to each of you."

"Let's all eat and have a rest," someone called.

"And of course a drink," interrupted a tipsy voice from the bar.

"Okay," acknowledged the first speaker, "A drink as well but a rest and then go as soon as the driver feels rested enough. He's the one that's been working." A disorganised utterance of 'ayes' and 'yeahs' indicated some sort of acceptance.

"The kiddies are asleep. Might as well wait awhile," said one of the pantomime mothers.

Joe had snatched the opportunity to sit and talk over past times with Carol while Jim enjoyed just enough drink and food and fell asleep in the chair. Slowly they too relaxed and drifted off to sleep until they were awakened to face an overwhelming fried breakfast.

Under a brightening sky at 7 a.m. the re-assembled train became alive with passengers, smoke and steam, and ready for the journey to Whitby. It was a pleasing revelation for Joe to discover that his A8 had to accompany the train on its journey to Whitby West Cliff station.

Carol took the opportunity to visit the footplate of 9885 and reminisce about when she had been a willing and scheming stowaway on their passenger train through Sandsend and Kettleness tunnels. They laughed as they recalled the countless ways Jim had tried to get her off the engine unseen.

"The Directors' train was the best laugh," said Joe.

"I thought the funniest one was at Sandsend," said Carol, "when Jim was trying to stop the train at the platform for me to get off and the engine at the front had forgotten to slow down. He'd either forgotten to stop or Joe had forgotten to tell him. Which was it Joe?" she asked.

"If I told you that, you'd be as wise as me." He turned to Jim, "Come on Jim. Get her off here before she causes trouble between us."

"But can't I ride on the footplate to Whitby with you Jim?" she asked mischievously. "I'm getting used to it?"

"Not with me you're not. It would be a sacking job this time."

Carol joined the train and with the passengers on board, the two engines, and the much depleted Woodley's Bakehouse consignment, set off for Whitby West Cliff station. They passed the scene of their 'nightmare in the snow' with cheers ringing out from the passengers and triumphant whistles from each of the two locomotives. The drifts had been cleanly cut through by their earlier efforts so they sped quickly on their way to Whitby West Cliff station.

They exchanged a few words with Carol and the Whitby crew and then had to leave for Castlebrough. Joe felt sure that he would see her again soon in Castlebrough in one week's time. He pledged to himself that he would seek her out. The next thought that drifted into his mind made him make another silent pledge. 'I've got to sort something out about Katiya if I'm taking up with Carol'.

★ ★ ★ ★

3
Full Steam Ahead.

"Tom, will tha' shunt the coal stage. Alan's right out." Bill Clarke was out in the shed yard speaking to Tom West on the small J72 shunting engine 9016. "We don't want to leave the stage wi' out coal for tomorrow morning."

The job was only going to take a few minutes, that was the hope but Alan, on the coal stage, had a message for Joe. "Odd you should come up now Joe. The two guys at the gate have been waiting for you to come into the yard. They were hoping to see you tonight."

"Two guys?" Joe looked up towards the wicket gate, "They could've waited for me in the messroom."

The darkness of the early evening shrouded the detail of the figures in spite of the nearby street gas light.

"They're not railway, one of them's foreign," said Alan Harker. Then he shouted "Mister!" to the men. "Come down here, young Wade's here."

"I'll look after things for you," Tom West his driver was definite. "Go and see your mates."

"Mates! They ain't my mates."

"Who are they then?"

"Don't know 'em from Adam."

"You'd better go and see them. If it's private get yuh sen in Alan's cabin. I'll put engine away. See you in the messroom."

When one of the two asked, "You Josef Wade?" Joe knew that he was speaking to a Russian, he'd heard the accent before. He recalled that his loco mates had said that a Ukrainian had been seeking to meet him. Could this be who they meant? Joe had been inclined to put the man's existence down to the mischievous imagination of his mates. He answered "Yes" and nervously led the way from the gate to the coal stage and the cabin.

"I to see you Mister Wade," said the one who'd already spoken.

Joe's hesitant short response was followed by the other shorter of the two figures who said in a clear English voice, "Piotr Borisovitch Maisky does not speak much English yet. That is why I have been helping him contact you."

"I'm puzzled why you want to see me," said Joe. "This isn't some lark the lads have got up. Is it?" At that moment the coalman tipped a quarter-ton of coal down the coal chute onto a noisy waiting engine. A cloud of coal-dust and steam drifted around Joe and through the light thrown by the solitary gas lamp. Tom West noisily withdrew the empty coal wagons from the high level coal stage and clattered down the bank. Joe insisted on seeking the quiet of the small wooden cabin. For a moment he wondered whether he was wise to enter the cabin with the two men, there was still the threat that the Russian might want to harm him.

"Let me tell you about Piotr Borisovich. He is a wounded Red Army soldier, in the Soviet Army," started the fluent English speaker.

"Who are you?" asked Joe smartly. "Are you Russian?"

"Sorry, I am an officer of the British-Soviet Society, I'm Bill Wright, I'm English. I'm working together with the Red Cross and the Town Council to help the refugee immigrants in Castlebrough." Joe's 'Yes, Yes,' hurried him on. "Piotr Borisovitch wants to speak with you about Katiya. He was taken prisoner in Western Poland at the end of the war - last April. That's when he was badly wounded. At the battle for Warsaw." The three entered the small wooden cabin and sat around the table before they tried to continue. They had privacy and a measure of quiet.

"Katiya, where does she fit into this?" asked Joe feeling a little nervous but also stimulated. 'A Red Army soldier', he thought excitedly. He'd read about them, seen them on the films. He thought of them as champions in the struggle against Nazism. Here was one in real life, in Castlebrough. But he looked so ordinary.

"Katiya thought he was dead," said the soldier's companion. "She'd been taken to Germany as a forced worker, a foreign labourer they called them, for nearly three years." The Russian then spoke quickly in his own language into his companion's ear. Bill Wright listened and Joe caught the words 'Sovyetsky passport'. Bill Wright continued, "She thought that Piotr had been killed in the Ukraine at the start of the war. At the battle for Kiev. But the Red Cross traced Katiya while he was in an American hospital and arranged for him to come here."

"What's he want?" asked Joe.

"Tovarrich, we friends." Piotr Borisovitch interrupted, pointing first to Joe's chest and then his own. "Katiya's Sovyetsky passport." He struggled with his few words of English then spoke again in his own language to his friend.

"Piotr asks about you and Katiya. What is she to you? Do you want to marry her?" he asks.

"I don't want to marry Katiya! or anyone." Joe was alarmed, he felt as though he was being pressurised into marriage. He rose in his seat, then calmed down and slowly and laboriously emphasised in the Russian soldier's direction, "I do not want to marry Katiya."

"Passport Sovyetsky, Katiya's passport? Pozhal'sta give to me." Borisovitch stressed, "You have."

"She gave me that - er, memento. She said she could not use it now. She had been German and now English." Clearly the Red Army man did not like Joe's hesitation, he spoke to him in Russian, with bits of English and explained but Joe didn't understand.

"Pozhal'sta?" The Russian addressed Joe.

"Please?" he says. "For the passport, he means. He expects that you still have it."

Joe nodded. "Of course. I still have it. You want it. But it is not yours. It is Katiya's."

"He needs it to take Katiya back to the Ukraine," explained Bill Wright.

Joe surrendered, after all had been considered it was only of passing interest to him, he wasn't prepared to argue about it. Discretion dictated that decision. "It's at my home. Yes. Yes. You can have the Soviet passport back for Katiya."

"Khorosho, Danke schon," the Red Army man also spoke the German word for thank you.

"Can you come with me tonight to my home?" Joe asked. Borisovitch spoke through his helper, who translated with difficulty. "We'll come to your house and bring Katiya. Tomorrow. Katiya will be pleased that you understand about her marriage. Have you any other things belonging to Katiya?"

"Only a babushka doll and a photograph. And two letters in German. They were my German lessons. Yes, I'll give you them all. I have a new girl friend."

Joe wasn't keen on them visiting his house and he was puzzled, even a bit threatened by the reference to her marriage. He remembered his Father's alarm on receiving the threatening letter.

Joe was flustered. "I'll take you to the house now," he said. The coalman had entered the cabin and Joe found himself nervously introducing the two visitors to the coalman. "Will you tell Katiya I have been ill? I thought to visit her tomorrow. It is Christmas Eve." He was anxiously wondering whether Katiya had to get married. If she had to it had nothing to do with him. He mustered up the courage to ask the English helper, "Is she to be a mother?" The puzzled response, "I don't think so," went some way towards easing his worry, Joe discussed the issue in his head. He had only been her friend, he had only been interested in her part in the War, and in learning

German from her. He didn't need the situation spelling out to him. He knew of lads who'd had to get married whilst protesting, "Not me."

The walk down to the shed improved the understanding between them. He learnt that Piotr had been a locomotive fireman in the Soviet Ukraine and was interested in the locomotives in the shed. Joe showed them around the shed as though the place belonged to him. They paused close by the messroom door and Joe used the opportunity to ask Bill Wright about Piotr Borisovitch's comment about Joe understanding about Katiya's marriage.

"Sorry, I thought you understood. Katiya is Piotr's wife. They married four years ago just as Germany invaded the Soviet Union. She is Mrs Piotr Borisovitch Maisky. He's come to take her home."

Relief flooded through Joe, then he wondered if Piotr was mad with him for being Katiya's friend. "Why hadn't she told me?"

Tom West came out from the messroom and broke into the conversation. "I've been waiting for you," he shouted towards Joe. "You big cloth-head. I'm going to the Mere Club?" He then directed his speech towards the two with Joe. "He's a bother, alus missing when you want him, or reading." Tom turned back into the messroom and again addressed Joe. "Bill Branson came to see you Joe. You're a bit of a bloody celebrity, alus someone wanting to see yuh. More folks after you than flies around a honey-pot."

"Cut the cackle, Tom. What's Bill Branson got to say?" asked Joe.

"He sez you've got your full money for that accident time-off. He only called in 'cos he was on his way down to the Mere Club. Probably hoping you're going to buy him a pint for his bother. N.U.R. men are like that," he grinned. "He's N.U.R." he said poking Joe in the chest.

"He's a bit queer too. He's A.S.L.E.F." Joe poked Tom in the chest playfully.

"You should get your head screwed on and leave the N.U.R. and join A.S.L.E.F. - a proper union. You could come and buy me a drink too."

"I will Tom. Do you two feel like a drink of English beer? Joe asked Bill Wright and Piotr."

"Da. Pivo, - - Inglish beer." The Russian words were followed by his faltering translation of pivo and his raising of an imaginary glass, then, "na zdaroviye."

"Cheers, - good health," responded the grinning Joe raising his imaginary glass.

He briefly introduced the Soviet soldier and the official from the British Soviet Society to Tom and the others in the messroom.

"Russian eh?" questioned Tom rhetorically. "That's coincidence Joe. Tommorow we're taking a train load of Russian timber for store at Snainton and Sawdon. It's for the building of new housing estates around Castlebrough."

"We might pick something up for Christmas," said Joe. "A rabbit, some eggs or a chicken. Mek a nice present for me Mam."

"Summat for your tea tomorrow on Christmas eve. Is yuh Dad home?"

"Me Dad, Tim and Luke. Luke's in the RAF now but he's home for Christmas. Tim's demobbed out of the RAF. Working as a wood machinist at Caxton's, he's got a bairn and a wife. They're living in our front room."

"That's all your family home. First Christmas together for a long time isn't it? There'll be a lot of families wi' empty chairs this Christmas." Tom waved his arms as though he was going to jump off somewhere, "Yuh ought to be having a party. Are you stoppin' in or goin' out?"

"Me Mam asked me that. She said 'can't you stop in for once?' I said 'I would.' Truth is, Tom, I got a conscience when she was looking after me when I had that accident. She's looked after me so many times when I've been ill. I never say 'Thank you'."

"Do summat special like, at your house, surprise her, and the family. Christmas is for saying thanks."

"I can't do that. Don't know what special is except buying Dad a tie for Christmas and Mam a pinny. An' I should be seeing Dan. Can't if I stop in."

"Dan'll come up to see you. I'll see to that. We'll think o' summat."

When the four of them walked into the Mere Club, Tom said, "I'll have a drink with my mates over there." He pointed in the direction of his waiting friends. "See yuh in the morning on that timber train. Don't be late. It's Christmas Eve tomorrow."

"I'm going to have a drinks with Bill and Piotr and my mates over there. Piotr Borisovich is okay," he said. He nearly told Tom about Katiya being married but caution dictated silence. He knew what the lads would have made of the knowledge.

★ ★ ★ ★

Christmas Evening, Castlebrough 1945, had the makings of a more joyous celebration than had been seen since 1939. The decorative lights were illuminated on the seafront, cinemas had 'House Full' signs, shops had more goods and the public houses were riotous and full of noise and colour from early in the day.

The countryside on the Pickering line was bright and green though the trees were leafless. The weather was so mild that memory of the early December snowfall that had suddenly immobilised the North's transport and trapped the Whitby bound passenger train at Hawsker was like a dream. Today was as if Spring was in the air.

The delivery of the timber train to Snainton reminded Joe of Carmel and Klaus the prisoner of war. 'Carmel must have died', he thought. He had not heard of her and she had stopped writing. Joe had not been down this line for many months. Her house was as it always had been but Carmel's figure was missing from the window. He asked the station porter for news of the crossing-keeper's daughter. "She went to hospital an' was given some of that new drug, made from cheese, Penicillin, I think they call it. She got better."

"Where is she?" asked Joe.

"She's with her Mam now at the signal cabin. Only got home for Christmas yesterday."

When he saw Carmel and her Mother walking down the platform he waved and later paid them a visit in their crossing-keeper's house. He learned of Carmel's new treatment and her gradual recovery, of her belief that Klaus's rose gold cross, which she still exhibited, had played a part in her recovery. Joe left, feeling glad and pleased, and loaded with country produce and new baking by Carmel and her Mother. It would be useful tonight for the event he and Tom were planning together.

His gifts from Carmel looked impressive on the draining board in the drab green-painted kitchen at home. He presented them to his Mother with as much expression as if he'd just brought them from the shop, yet there was a new warmth in his heart for his mother and a better understanding of what he owed her. But he wasn't capable of saying "Thank you Mam," and giving her a kiss, he didn't understand that kind of expression.

Later in the day in the living room of the Wade's home, coloured paper chains criss-crossed the white-washed ceiling. A fire of wood off-cuts roared in the grate above which a horizontal strip of paper, pinned to the wall, carried the red-painted words 1945 CHRISTMAS WITHOUT WAR. On the small buffet the first Wade grandchild wailed on Tim's knee.

The black-out frames which had stood close by the window for the duration were absent, this and the quality and quantity of food on the table were indicators of a Christmas without war.

"I didn't expect you Mr West," Emily Wade blurted out, as she answered the knock on the back door. "And you Danny."

"Can we come in Mrs Wade? Sorry about me bein' in me working togs. Dan's here to see Joseph." Tom West helped his son pull the wheelchair through the door.

"I'm getting tea ready," flustered Joe's mother Emily.

"Don't bother we've got plenty," answered Tom mysteriously. "You knows Mrs Wade. Doesn't yuh? That Joe gets full pay for that time he was bad after that accident."

"Is that good?" Emily asked timidly. She was over-powered by Tom's quick movements and loud repartee.

"I'll say," replied Tom. "Mind you Mrs Wade, it was my union A.S.L.E.F. that pushed the N.U.R. into making a claim." He paused but not long enough to be interrupted. "Joe's in the N.U.R. He won't join us."

"I've never liked him being on those engines," said Joe's Mother. "That bang on his head could have been worse, could've killed him." She turned to her work in the kitchen. She couldn't understand the sudden appearance and entry of Dan and Tom West, except to conclude that it must have something to do with Joe who was absent as usual.

"Stop gabbing Dad, Joe's Mam doesn't want to hear your propaganda about A.S.L.E.F." said Dan.

"You shut up Dan," he retorted then looked towards the kitchen as someone opened the back door again. "Who is it?" Tom responded to the sound of Mrs Wade's uttered remark. "Somebody else."

"Tom Rittler, Ma'am," responded the newcomer. "Railway Guard extra-ordinary, that's me. Tom West and your Joe asked me to come and bring these."

"He's got some of Nesfield brewery's bottled bitter. Let him in Mrs," shouted Tom West.

Tom Rittler heard the call and responded, "I'm looking for you Tom, I've brought the victuals and the drink."

Tom heard Rittler and shouted from the living room. "Come in Tom, bring the victuals. Where's the flowers? Good, them's the best Christmas chrysanthemums from me own greenhouse from me and Danny."

The room and the kitchen were filling as family members from other parts of the house responded to the noise.

"We've just popped in - Christmas like - an' Victory Year. Joe organised us. Where's Joe? Missing again?" Tom grabbed Emily

Wade and planted a light kiss on her cheek and ceremoniously presented her with the bunch of chrysanthemums.

★ ★ ★ ★

Joe was missing from home again. He was in the 'Railway Tavern' with a uniformed Red Army soldier and Johnny Marsay but he was thinking of the impromptu party taking place at home. He had indeed organised the gathering as Tom had stated, he must have been mad, his plans were ad hoc and likely to fall apart. Why had he ever listened to Tom West about an impromptu Christmas 'do' a day before Christmas Day? Mother would be distraught by the invasion of the unexpected. He downed his pint of mild beer and put the empty glass on the tavern bar.

"We'd better go home, to my house." Joe spoke to his railway chum Johnny Marsay and he turned towards Katiya and the Red Army soldier Piotr Borisovitch to emphasise 'To my house'.

The Railway Tavern was full of railwaymen and servicemen in and out of uniform. Piotr was in uniform. He wore his Red Army khaki-brown battle dress with its Hammer and Sickle emblem and a C.A. shoulder flash indicating his membership of the Soviet Army. The soldier and the emblem were unusual to Castlebrough. His chest displayed two Soviet medals which recognised his bravery in battle. When Joe had heard the night before that Piotr had his army uniform with him he'd prevailed upon him to wear it in public and visit his home.

"I don't know why I got involved in this. I'm sure my Dad isn't going to like it," he confided in Johnny.

"It was your idea. You fixed it up, talked everybody into it. Even poor ole Father Wade is involved. And he doesn't know it yet," Johnny reminded him. "What about Katiya? I thought she was with you."

"No she's with Piotr Borisovitch."

The previous night in the Mere Social Club had been a big success, Katiya had been brought from home to join Piotr. The Club Committee had never before 'signed in' a Red Army soldier and his wife. The local people exploited the occasion to the full with song and dance. Piotr demonstrated the Cossack Dance and he and Katiya danced and sang the folk dances of the Ukrainian Republic. The success led to a strong invitation to Piotr, Katiya and Bill Wright to meet Joe and Johnny and go to a Christmas gathering at the Wade's home on Hastings Road. Alcohol did the planning. They still had not collected the 'Sovyetsky passport' and other mementos of Joe's time's with Katiya. That could be done at the same time.

★ ★ ★ ★

Joe nervously pushed into his Mother's kitchen with his four companions and watched his Mother stagger speechless at the sight of the strangers and the Red Army uniform. Suitable words were expressed as they passed into the living room where the baby still added to the hub hub.

"Dad! I've brought you a Soviet soldier, Piotr Borisovitch." Joe shouted his message directly to his Father who was in deep conversation with Tom Rittler about his small handful of gold sovereigns. Rittler traded gold sovereigns for resale at a profit. Most eyes were on the soldier or on Fred Wade but Joe's eyes settled on the red hair of Carol Blanchard. He was so surprised that he didn't understand or hear his Father's question to the Soviet soldier to whom he'd been roughly introduced.

"Carol Blanchard!" Joe called out and advanced towards her. She was with his uniformed younger brother Luke and Luke's girl friend Audrey. 'How had this come about?' He thought, 'And Katiya? He felt unsure, staggered, but the collective pressure of eager voices broke the momentary silence and welcoming hands sought out the Soviet soldier.

'I organised this?' Joe said to himself. 'Just by having a big mouth and Tom West.' He didn't believe it, but his house had never been so full of people, never experienced such an expression of rejoicing.

"Let's get steam up," Tom West was shouting. "Put some coal on Joe."

"Get some food everybody," Fred Wade followed him.

Someone started to sing 'Roll out the Barrel' and then drifted into the 'White Cliffs of Dover'. A faint 'We'll Meet Again' bravely surfaced and was lost as the hub-bub of conversation overwhelmed the efforts to sing.

"I say let's toast Joe's Mam. No. I mean let's toast Emily Wade. That's who she is." Tom West was shouting, trying to dominate the gathering. Emily Wade responded with a 'Don't be daft.' and sought to escape to her kitchen but Joe pushed her with a 'Go on Mam.' Somebody else directed her also. Tom West caught her pinafore and gently pulled her. Joe felt pleased for his thin harassed mother, she had never been in the spotlight in her life, at least as far as Joe knew. Now here she was with the big loud locoman Tom West who was intending to make a speech about her.

"Here's the woman of this house who kept this house going through the War while others were away. She found the food, and the medicines and the courage. Yes Emily, courage it took courage to keep going. A toast to Emily, the undimmed star of this household, Fred, and lads, and neighbours."

Piotr Borisovitch and Katiya called out, "Na zdaroviye," as they raised the drink that had been thrust into their hands.

"Good health," said Bill Wright in Joe's ear by way of translation.

The listeners saw a different Tom, he was becoming eloquent and emotional. He certainly didn't seem to be the brash, pushy, for ever loud and mobile Tom. Cups of tea, beer from mugs and the occasional jam jar raised up to Emily. Tom tried to keep on but the emotion drained from him.

"All the women fought on the Home Front. Don't forget there was a Women's Front, as well as the other fronts in the war," he said. Then he trailed off into, "You say summat Fred."

Luke pushed his Father forward. Joe hoped his Dad would say something, maybe because he had never felt so involved with his family before. He lived with them, but he was only beginning to see them all as people, not just, Mother, Brother or Father, but people with their own problems.

"The War is over, thank God we all say." Dad was on his feet calling for silence. "Let's get down to building a better life, no unemployment, good housing, and for God's sake no more War. There are lots of lads and lasses who aren't here now. Their chairs are empty." Everyone was quiet now, listening. "They are with us. Their chairs may be empty, but they are with us. They're here," he patted his chest, "and here," he touched his head. "Our Herbert's here. Our Herbert, killed at 27, young Gates, only 8 years old, the first to die in the bombing of Castlebrough. He's here."

"An' our Charlie," called out a voice. "Our Lucy and John," called another. "Our Don."

"And millions more. Up and down this land, across the seas, in the seas, countless thousands in watery graves." Dad was warming up. "Continents I did not know about until war swept like a fire across them have become the graves for millions who never thought to travel. They are all in the empty chairs and in our hearts. Let's remember them, as I remember our Herbert. You remember yours." Fred paused momentarily, turned to his wife and put his free arm across her shoulders in a warm embrace. "Brush the tears away Emily, and you Jack. I have them. We all have. Brush them away. We're out of the darkness now, out into the daylight once again. Times are going to be good, better than ever before. There'll always be full employment, and free hospitals and medicines. There's going to be peace. No more war." He emphasised more loudly, "No more war." Spontaneous applause punctuated his words. "Raise your hands and drinks in a sober salute and thank God for this Christmas without war."

"No more war," echoed some listeners.

"And to the Soviet soldier, to all Soviet soldiers, to all their empty chairs, aye, and the Soviet women, to all of the women," added Fred Wade. He pointed towards Piotr and Katiya and hands pushed them forwards as Fred Wade spoke. Piotr clapped his hands to dictate a rhythm speed to others, he touched the hands of many near him as he spun around and started to dance as only Russians seemed able to dance. Onlookers had to press back against the walls. His feet flashed from beneath his crouched body while his hands settled on his hips. A few brave but stiff bodies laughingly tried to emulate him.

Joe's Mother started to cry, "Why did you do this Joe? I can't stand it." Joe could not speak past the lump in his throat as his arms fell around his mother's thin shoulders. He tried to kiss her on the cheek, his lips were clumsy but he knew that he was expressing something tender and worthwhile to his Mother. Everybody clasped, or kissed, or hugged. Joe found himself looking into the brown eyes of Carol Blanchard in the company of his brother Luke and Audrey.

"How?" Joe asked. "It's great but what a shock."

She giggled mischievously. "How?" she asked rhetorically and continued, "I met your Luke with my friend Audrey in town." She pushed Audrey playfully and they both laughed. "They were coming to your house, I decided to stow away with them. I'd done it once before hadn't I." She grinned, her red hair framed her face, their cheeks touched and their lips found each others. They were closer together than at any time since he'd met her.

He grinned back. "Glad you learnt a bit about stowing away. I'll give our Luke a medal for bringing you."

"He didn't bring me. I came here under my own steam even if I did have to hook on to another train."

Joe moved suddenly and pulled Carol towards him. "Merry Christmas," he said and kissed her suddenly, "And a Happy New Year." They embraced and she kissed back and uttered the same seasonal wish.

"There's steam coming out of your ears," said Luke pulling him away and grasping Carol to himself and wishing her a Merry Christmas.

Joe led her to the passage at the foot of the stairs. "It's easier to talk here," he said as they leaned against the wall.

"I thought you'd never ask." She didn't move as he folded her in his arms, but then gently she withdrew. "Just a moment. What about your German girl?"

"The blonde girl, Katiya, she's with her husband.?"

"Who's her husband?"

"The Russian Soldier. You saw him dancing? She's going back to Russia with him. They were married in 1941 just before Germany invaded Russia. He told me that on parting they swore to meet again. She swore never to tell anybody that she was the wife of a Soviet soldier because the Nazis were killing soldiers' wives."

"What was your interest in her?"

"I was teaching her English. And she was teaching me German. It was my bit of War Work."

His arms took her again, there was no resistance. "I'll believe you when thousands wouldn't," she said. "Pity we aren't marooned on a train all night in a snow-drift."

"You're here now. That's what's important. How did it happen?"

"I've told you, it's the power of steam. I've had a full head of steam since the night in the snow storm. I've been all steamed up ever since." They giggled and he sensed the warmth of her body and her willingness to be close.

"What do think caused it?" he repeated softly as he felt her breath on his cheek.

"I did. You'd have never found time. Why do you think I suggested to Dad to settle in Castlebrough?"

"Are we on track for better things then?" Joe asked.

She laughed and pushed him away. "Steady as you go. Wait for the signals."

THE END